This Won't Hurt: A History of the Hospitals of Lichfield

This Won't Hurt

A History of the Hospitals of Lichfield

by Mary Hutchinson,
Ingrid Croot and Anna Sadowski

Published by
Lichfield Hospitals History Group
25 Chapel Lane, Lichfield WS14 9BA

ISBN 978-0-9565225-0-4

Typeset by Workspace, Lichfield
Printed by Book Printing Services, Keele University, ST5 5BG

This book is dedicated to all of the people who have worked over the years in roles both paid and unpaid to improve and support the health and well-being of the people of this area.

Special recognition must go to Mrs Ellen Leighfield and Mr David Budden whose earlier works on the history of the hospitals have been so valuable in the production of the book.

Table of Contents

Page

Foreword

It is a real pleasure to be asked to provide some introductory words towards this wonderful book on the history of the hospitals of Lichfield.

We forget the past at our peril. The monastic beginnings of our hospitals, based upon strong values and compassion, when medicine was little more than placebo, are all too relevant today, especially in the context of a modern technological health service that sometimes forgets the individual and his or her perspective and hopes, and of an NHS, which we have all begun to take for granted.

I owe personally a huge depth of gratitude to local community hospitals. Many members of my family have been treated successfully in our community hospitals and many of my own patients have never had to go anywhere else. Indeed, my youngest daughter was the very last caesarean section in our local community hospital.

It will always be attractive for patients to be looked after in their local hospital by local doctors and nurses, who are instantly familiar simply because they are part of the local community. As we begin to talk about the sustainability of the NHS and the 'big society', community hospitals will become ever more important as a focus of local effort. They are a means of everyone having a role and an expression of the importance of every local clinician, manager and patient in making things better – especially for those in our communities, who are most in need.

The history of Britain's community hospitals is a triumph. The history of the Samuel Johnson Community Hospital in Lichfield is a double triumph because it has survived to tell the story and because it is the living example of how a local community can best look after its own.

Dr Michael Dixon
General Practitioner and Chair of the NHS Alliance

Preface

Imagine a life without places of refuge and comfort, and without resources to care for the needy and sick.

At its inception, the Victoria Hospital delivered state of the art care, a microcosm of hospitals found in London and other large cities.

However, the development of accessible district general hospitals and more sophisticated technology meant that increasing numbers of patients could receive care appropriate to the 21st century. In October 2001, it was announced that the Victoria Hospital, affectionately known as the Vic, was to close. There was no reprieve for the old lady. No amount of fundraising was to rescue the place that was built by the people of Lichfield – donated brick by brick.

Why do we need a book about the history of this hospital and others in the surrounding areas of Lichfield? What was their importance, who did they serve and what about the people who worked there and the patients they saw? This book traces the history of all the hospitals around and in Lichfield and the important place they held in society.

Many, if not all, citizens of Lichfield have been patients at least once. The staff, many living close by, offered help and comfort when it was needed. Some had even been born in the maternity unit themselves. Whilst the reason for going to hospital was not usually a happy one, you could be sure someone would be waiting to help you.

Our goal is to bring some of the stories to light, to allow the reader to share the experiences of those who played an important part in shaping health care in Lichfield. We spoke to former staff members, doctors, nurses and patients alike. What did they remember and what stood out for them?

We look at why these hospitals were built, thus ensuring that, whilst the buildings may have been demolished or changed function, their importance will not be quickly forgotten. Does it matter? The answer has to be yes, it does, because they were the foundation stones of the future.

1: Victoria Hospital by John Clayton

List of Illustrations

Front Cover

Top left - Victoria Hospital
Top right - St Michael's Hospital
Bottom right - Hammerwich Hospital
Bottom left - St Matthew's Hospital
Badge awarded to enrolled nurses trained at St Michael's

> ❛ It may seem a strange principle to enunciate as the very first requirement in a Hospital that it should do the sick no harm. ❜

Florence Nightingale (1820-1910)

1: Setting the Scene
A Brief History of Hospitals

As early as 4000BC religions identified certain holy beings with the ability to heal. This encouraged the building of temples as places of healing. That these temples were medical schools in their earliest form is beyond question.

The Romans established hospitals for the sick and for injured soldiers. Later, a hospital was often part of a religious order or a community such as an abbey or monastery. Reference to this can be found in the way that those who delivered care were addressed as 'Sister' or 'Brother'.

Wherever there was large population growth, hospitals were founded, which is not so surprising, because with increasing numbers of people and lack of sanitation came disease. There was a real need for places to confine and treat contagious diseases, such as plague, cholera and typhoid.

However, the modern concept of hospitals dates from AD331, when Constantine, having been converted to Christianity, abolished all pagan hospitals, where the ill were isolated from the community. A new way of caring for the sick had to be established. Christian tradition emphasized the close relationship of the sufferer to his fellow man, upon whom rested the obligation for care. Illness thus became a matter for the Christian church and the care of the sick was placed above and before every other Christian duty.

This concept was not exclusive to Christianity. Arab hospitals admitted patients regardless of religious belief, race, or social order. In the 7th century more attention was given to the well-being of the patient's soul than to curing bodily ailments. The manner in which monks cared for their own sick became a model for those outside the order. The monasteries had an infirmitorium, a place to which their sick were taken for treatment. They had a pharmacy and frequently a garden with medicinal plants. In addition to caring for sick monks and nuns, the monasteries opened their doors to pilgrims and to other travellers.

The growth of hospitals accelerated during the Crusades. A beautiful example is found in the Abbey of Fontevraud in the Loire region of France, where the legendary crusader, Richard the Lionheart, son of Henry II of England, is buried.

Military hospitals were established along well-travelled routes. The Knights Hospitallers of the Order of St John of Jerusalem in 1099 established in the Holy Land a hospital that could care for some 2,000 patients. St John's Ambulance Brigade is still with us today. In 1156, one of the first medical schools in Europe was established at Bologna – here public dissection was first practised. Religion continued to be the dominant influence in the establishment of hospitals during the Middle Ages.

St Bartholomew's Hospital (Barts) was founded about 1123 by

Rahere, a courtier and a cleric who was taken seriously ill while in Rome on a pilgrimage. He vowed that if he recovered he would build a hospital. Restored to health and back in England, he was able to get Henry I to provide a site at Smithfield in the City of London and there the famous St Bartholomew's was so dedicated, because the saint had appeared in a vision to Rahere during his illness.

The history of one early Lichfield 'hospital' begins in 1129 when Roger de Clinton was appointed Bishop of Lichfield. As well as building a cathedral, he built a defensive ditch and gates (or barrs) around the southern part of the city, and enlisted soldiers to man it. Pilgrims and travellers who arrived late at night were not allowed into the city, and so he built a priory just outside Culstubbe Gate. It was completed in 1135 and thus there came into being the Hospital of St John the Baptist Without the Barrs of the City of Lichfield, which survives today as a handsome building on the corner of St

2: St John's Hospital

John Street and Birmingham Road. Its courtyard and chapel offer quiet respite to any visitor, and it is home to a number of retired men and married couples of the Anglican faith. Its title of hospital was more closely linked to the hospitality provided, rather than any medical care.

Similarly, another of Lichfield's oldest buildings, which still continues to provide a safe home for those in need, is Milley's Hospital in Beacon Street. This timbered building, almost opposite the entrance to the Cathedral Close, originated in 1424 when William Heyworth, Bishop of Lichfield and Coventry, endowed a hospital for 10 poor, elderly women of the city. Thomas Milley, after whom it was named, increased its revenues and rebuilt the hospital in 1504. Over the years the building has been reconstructed and rebuilt and today provides accommodation in small, self-contained flats.

There are few diseases in the history of mankind which elicit more anxiety, fear and revulsion than leprosy. And even in a modern, enlightened community one can still hear the faint echoes of the medieval response to its presence. The existence of leprosy in a medieval community was obviously a concern for all, but the task of identifying the leper remained the responsibility of the clergy. The Bible stated that the disease was 'unclean'; therefore, isolation prevailed and intensified during the early Middle Ages.

In the 13th century, the monks and friars of the Hospital of St John the Baptist travelled, probably by mule, to administer to the inmates of St Leonard's Leper Hospital and burial ground at Freeford. A chapel adjoined the hospital to celebrate Mass and pray for souls. Also at this time, grants and casual gifts were made to the hospital by the Crown; for example, in 1246 Henry III gave to the 'lepers of Lichfield' 15 carcasses of salt pork from the stores in Nottingham Castle. On this site today, at the junction of Tamworth Road and Gorse Lane, stands Freeford House, a handsome brick and timber-framed house with two adjoining cottages, the furthest of which is thought to have been St Leonard's Chapel.

Lichfield can lay claim to a proud tradition of the protection of public health, because it was one of the first cities to have access to clean running water. In 1310, the Franciscan friars of Lichfield were beneficiaries of Henry Bellfounder who granted them access to his springs at Fowlewell near Aldershawe for their 'use and comfort'. They erected a conduit head and constructed pipes to convey the water to their friary – however at that time they could not give away 'even a small vessel of water without the donor's special permission'. Water was also being piped from springs at Pipe Hill into the cathedral and close from the 1100s. The townspeople could tap into this, and also the aqueduct that ran from the Cathedral Close to the market (Conduit Street).

On 3 January 1545, the Conduit Lands Trust was formed – its main purpose was the maintenance and improvement of Lichfield's pipes and aqueducts to ensure fresh water was available to the citizens of Lichfield. At that time, the water flowed via a conduit in Bird Street (the Crucifix), one in the Market Square (the Cross) and a third on the corner of Tamworth and Lombard Streets (Stone Cross). It is remarkable that the Conduit Lands Trust safeguarded this duty until 1963, when the Trust sold its remaining shares in the water undertaking to South Staffordshire Waterworks Company. Although no longer concerned with supplying water, it continues to function as a charity; the trustees have been extensively involved in public works, as well as education.

3: Lichfield Conduit

The Middle Ages also saw the beginnings of support for hospital-like institutions established by secular authorities. Towards the end of the 15th century, many cities and towns supported some kind of institutional health care; it has been said that in England there were no less than 200 such establishments that met a growing social need. This gradual transfer of responsibility for institutional health care from the church to civil authorities continued in England after the dissolution of the monasteries by Henry VIII $c.1540$, which put an end to hospital building in England for some 200 years.

The loss of monastic hospitals in England caused individual philanthropists to provide for the sick, the injured, and the handicapped, thus laying the foundation for the voluntary hospital movement. The first voluntary hospital in England was probably established in London in 1718 by Huguenots from France, and was closely followed by the foundation of such London hospitals as the Westminster Hospital in 1719, Guy's Hospital in 1724, and the London Hospital in 1740. Between 1736 and 1787 hospitals were established outside London in at least 18 cities.

In 1766 Staffordshire General Infirmary opened in Stafford. The following year the Lichfield Corporation subscribed 20 guineas to this institution, thereby becoming a trustee of the infirmary, entitled to recommend two in-patients a year, as well as any number of out-patients. By 1803 a dispensary for the poor, supported by subscription, existed in Lichfield. In 1831 the St Mary's Select Vestry (a number of persons chosen to represent and manage the concerns of the parish for one year) voted the dispensary the following amounts:

- £10 to supply medicine to the poor of the parish
- £5 for a physician to give occasional advice to the poor
- £5 for a surgeon to be in attendance

At the same time the vestry stopped its annual subscription to Stafford Infirmary as it considered the dispensary competent to provide the same assistance.

In 1699 the Conduit Lands trustees paid George Hector £5 for attending nine people; he set several broken bones and cured a scrofulous neck tumour (a disease with glandular swellings, probably a form of tuberculosis). From 1727 to 1728 a total of

£16.4s.6d. was paid to 'Mr. Hammond for physic given to poor inhabitants at this very sickly time'. Erasmus Darwin provided the poor with medical help as well as food and other assistance during his time in Lichfield from 1756 to 1781. In 1828 J. T. Law, Master of St John's Hospital and Chancellor of the Diocese, abolished pew rents in the hospital chapel and asked those who had been paying to give the money instead for the provision of medical help for the poor who suffered accidents or sudden illness.

Lichfield has been home to two eminent physicians – Sir John Floyer and Erasmus Darwin – whose influence was widespread, and whose work is still commemorated today.

Sir John Floyer (1649 – 1734) came from Hints, a village between Lichfield and Tamworth, and read medicine at Queen's College, Oxford. He came to Lichfield in 1680 and played a leading role in the community. In 1686 he was elected a Justice of the Peace for life; later he was elected bailiff. The circumstances of his knighthood are shrouded in uncertainty. He was probably knighted by James II, in whose political intrigues he is usually presumed to have participated. Since he was only on the threshold of his medical career, the honour of knighthood is thought to have been conferred for political rather than medical activities. Floyer developed a new understanding of the workings of the human body and approaches to care. He was a careful observer of people, collecting and recording data. Although many of Floyer's patients were wealthy, he also used knowledge gleaned from the local peasants and elderly men living in St John's Hospital. Some of his most important contributions to medical research were related to the human pulse, the efficacy of cold baths, the investigation of asthma and other respiratory ailments, and care of the elderly. A ward is named after Sir John Floyer in Good Hope Hospital, Sutton Coldfield.

Erasmus Darwin (1731 – 1802) was born at Elston Hall, near Newark, Nottinghamshire, the youngest of four sons. After attending St John's College, Cambridge, he underwent medical education at Edinburgh Medical School. He became one of the foremost physicians of his time; indeed King George III asked him to be his personal physician but Darwin declined, preferring to stay where he had settled in Lichfield.

Darwin not only had extensive knowledge of the structure and workings of the human body, but also extraordinary learning in the fields of physics, chemistry, geology, meteorology and all aspects of biology. With his ability to make friends, he soon built up a vast network of associates – men and women like himself who independently became known as the leading scientific and philosophical lights of their time. With contacts like Matthew Boulton, Josiah Wedgwood, and James Watt he set up the Lunar Society, which became the main intellectual powerhouse of the Industrial Revolution in England. His colleague and friend, William Withering, pioneered the use of digitalis in the treatment of heart disease.

Erasmus Darwin's home in Lichfield, in the Cathedral Close, is now a museum dedicated to his life's work.

In 1817, Lichfield was described as an open handsome city. However, as long-distance travel became more common and communications between the major cities increased, Lichfield grew in popularity as a stopping-off point, and by the late 18th century a procession of coaches would be rattling into the city daily. During the 19th century Lichfield's population, both resident and temporary, grew further.

By the end of the 19th century, there were major changes in

medicine and nursing. Because of advances in medicine, hospitals became places to get better and to improve the quality of life of the sick and injured. They were no longer simply holding places to contain disease. In the 20th century, some hospitals were founded to deal with specific illnesses, often related to local industry. These institutions were financed by gifts and sometimes specialised in the kind of care given.

Our story continues with the history of the hospitals that have served the people of Lichfield and outlying villages from the 19th century until the present day.

> '...pains and diseases of the mind are only cured by Forgetfulness, Reason but skins the wound, which is perpetually liable to fester again. '

Erasmus Darwin (1731-1802)

2: Care of the Insane and the Evolution of St Matthew's Hospital

The history of care of the insane is closely interwoven with that of the poor in general. As society attempted to help the poor and treat the insane, their lives became increasingly regimented and institutionalised. At the turn of the 18th century, the process had scarcely begun (exceptions were to be found in London and Bristol), and for the insane there had been little help or intervention of any kind. The well-to-do might be attended at home, as for any other illness, by a general physician. If the disorder proved intractable or the patient unmanageable, he or she might be admitted to one of the few small private madhouses which had begun to be set up in the 17th century, and catered for more than one patient at a time. These places rapidly expanded in number to become the largest single providers of institutional care of the insane until the mid-19th century. Increasingly, the private fee-paying patients were supplemented by paupers who were boarded out by their parishes; in the provinces in particular, this boarding out became the normal method of providing for parish lunatics.

About 1775 George Chadwick, a physician, appears to have begun using his house in St John Street for the confinement of lunatics. In 1778 he was licensed by the Quarter Sessions to receive up to 10 patients there. Erasmus Darwin and a justice inspected the house in 1779 and found conditions to be good. By 1787 Chadwick was charging an entrance fee of one guinea, £17 for the first year, and £14 for the second year on condition that the patient had not been troublesome. A peak of 23 patients is recorded in 1808. In 1811 the inspectors reported that patients in close confinement were kept in dirty conditions with insufficient straw, though Chadwick protested that the inspection was made on a Saturday morning a few hours before the rooms were due to be cleaned. In 1814 the license was not renewed; however, three years later, in 1817, a license for an asylum was granted to Thomas Rowley, a surgeon living in St John Street.

In 1818, Rowley transferred the asylum to a house dating from the 18th century, known as Sandfields Lodge on Fosseway Lane. Although he continued to own the asylum, it was managed by a series of superintendents until 1846, when he sold it following notification from the inspectors that the establishment was unsatisfactory. In particular, the dormitories outside the house, which were occupied by the pauper lunatics, were cold and damp. In 1854 the asylum was owned and run by Dr H. Lynch with two classes of patients; the first class were charged £80 a year upwards and the second, £50. There were 11 private patients in 1855; there were also 13 paupers occupying outside buildings and the inspectors recommended that they should be brought into the house. On further visits in December they found the place so dirty, cold and neglected that in 1856 the Lunacy Commissioners urged the withdrawal of the license and the asylum duly closed.

In England, there was no lunacy legislation until 1744, when a bill for 'regulating madhouses' was passed to regulate private asylums, in which abuses were prevalent. The Act was not effective, since anyone could get a licence to open an asylum. The Royal College of Physicians of London received reports of abuses, but could do little. This Act also authorised any two justices to apprehend pauper lunatics, who could be detained, possibly chained, ill-clad or even naked, in filthy conditions. Against that shameful and sickening background, a quiet revolution in the care of the insane was wrought by William Tuke, a Quaker layman, who opened an establishment named 'The Retreat' in York in the late 18th century. Here he introduced humane principles, where cure of the lunatic might be achieved through kindness, work, discipline and religion – in short, a restoration of dignity for the individual. Restraint was kept to a minimum.

In the early 19th century, another major factor in bringing mental illness to public attention was the illness of George III, a popular monarch who suffered recurrent periods of mania (probably caused by porphyria) that his physicians were unable to control. They sought the advice of the Rev. Dr Francis Willis, who ran an asylum in Lincolnshire. He is said to have told the king that he was in urgent need of medical treatment, because his ideas were deranged, and that he must control himself or be put in a straitjacket. The prominence of the king's illness and its treatment focused attention on the problem and led to general questioning about the lunacy laws. The attempt by a lunatic to shoot the king in a Drury Lane theatre precipitated action and the outcome led to the passage of a bill in 1808, usually referred to as Wynn's Act – 'for the better care and maintenance of lunatics being paupers or criminals in England'.

Under this Act, magistrates were allowed to build a rate-supported asylum in each county to cope with the large number of pauper lunatics. As the Act was discretionary, only nine English counties complied, but concern for the plight of the mentally ill was increasing. The first county asylum was opened in 1812 in Nottinghamshire, and by 1841, a further 13 had been added. The Staffordshire County Asylum, now known as St George's Hospital in Stafford, was opened in 1818, having 120 beds. However, the need rapidly outstripped the supply and by 1848 nearly 250 patients were being squeezed in. By this time, the 1845 Lunatics Act had been created, primarily by Lord Shaftsbury, who, motivated by deeply held Christian convictions, had laboured long and hard on behalf of the afflicted.

The 1845 Act also regulated the admission of patients. Private patients were given protection from collusion between certifying doctors while the form for a pauper patient was to be signed by a magistrate or clergyman as well as by the relieving officer of the Workhouse Union. The superintendent of each asylum was to keep careful records of all admissions, diagnoses, discharges, escapes, transfers and deaths. He was also required to report all occasions on which restraint or seclusion of any patient had been found necessary.

In 1854 Coton Hill Hospital opened, but this was exclusively for private patients and the need for extra accommodation for paupers remained a pressing problem. Thus another county asylum, built at Burntwood, was opened on 20 December 1864. The estate, consisting of about 94 acres, had cost £6,963. When the first patients arrived at this new asylum, only the west wing providing 240 beds for male patients had been built, alongside the kitchen, dining hall, offices, workshops and laundry. Above the dining hall, the asylum originally had its own chapel, seating 315 in highly polished pews; there was

4: St Matthew's Hospital

also a cemetery. The water supply came from a series of wells sunk locally, with the sewage initially decomposing in a smelly open pit, ultimately remedied in the 1880s. At the outset, the asylum was lit by paraffin lamps which were a fire risk. Within a few months of opening, a gas plant was established and the gas was used for cooking and lighting from an early date. Not until 1904 was electricity used for lighting, when a steam-powered generating plant was purchased.

Lord Shaftsbury exerted pressure on workhouse officials to transfer their insane inmates to the newly built asylums and this largely accounted for the dramatic rise in the asylum population. However, as numbers exceeded space available, many were 'boarded out' to other asylums having spare room. Thus a number of patients from Stafford had been 'boarded out' to Chester. When the Burntwood Asylum opened they were brought back as boarding out was expensive!

The east wing containing the female wards was completed in 1868. Strictly separated from the men, it extended the accommodation to a total of 530 beds. This more than met the immediate needs; other counties not so favourably placed were desperately seeking accommodation for their surplus lunatics and thus there was an opportunity to make a profit. In 1871 there were 491 patients and a staff of four officers, 41 attendants and nurses, and five artisans.

All asylums were regularly inspected by two commissioners, a medical practitioner and a barrister, whose yearly visits were unannounced. The prime objectives of the commissioners were to ensure that staff were complying with legislation, that standards of care were comparable and acceptable, and to convey information about new developments elsewhere, thus encouraging improvements. Every patient was interviewed, and the commissioners listened to their complaints. The state of the building was carefully inspected;

5: Female Wards, St Matthew's Hospital

enquiries were made into the type of education provided and the number of patients being usefully employed. Medical notes were examined and comments made on their quality, and enquiries were made into the religious services provided and the number of patients attending. Clearly, the commissioners' reports carried much weight and were carefully considered, not only by the asylum directors but also at Home Office level.

In *An Account of the Asylum for the Insane*, published in 1825, Waln wrote, 'The treatment of insanity… is divided into two parts; they are generally called the moral and medical treatment…'

The 'moral treatment' of the insane required space, fresh air and pastimes as well as religious worship, exercise, or work for the physically fit. In its heyday, to occupy the inmates and to provide supplies, the lunatic asylum at Burntwood had a farm. The first mention of this is found in the committee minutes of February 1866, when the builder was engaged to build six pigsties. Clearly the doctor's duties were broader than those of today, because Dr Davis, the first medical superintendent, was authorised to purchase two cows at a sum not exceeding £40.

On Lady Day (25 March: the Feast of the Annunciation) in 1870, the nearby Coulter Lane Farm, with its farm buildings and 72 acres of land became part of the asylum estate. By the 1890s the farm consisted of about 150 acres with extensive outbuildings, piggeries and cowsheds. In 1935 Fulfen Farm with 40 acres of land was added.

Every year, from 1881, Wintertons of Lichfield were engaged to inspect the farm and give a valuation and every year they submitted a glowing report of its condition and the state of the livestock. Later on the farm became a major part of the asylum activities, providing work for many patients and contributing a large proportion of the meat, vegetables, eggs and milk required in the asylum.

A bakery, shoemaker's shop, gas works, electricity plant and even a brewery (part of the pay for staff was a beer allowance!) were further added. A burial ground was consecrated in 1867 and extended in 1904. It remained in use until the 1920s, and its chapel was demolished in the 1960s. There were many extensions, notably in the late 1890s and the mid-1930s. The splendid chapel now standing to the south of the former hospital site was opened in 1900, and a nurses' home was built in 1914.

Medical treatment chiefly consisted of the liberal employment of blisters, purgatives, cupping and blood-letting based upon the hypothesis that insanity was a disease of malign strength or of active inflammation.

Little is known about the physical treatment of the insane patient, although commissioners' reports from the early 1880s record that walking and other gentle exercise proved more effectively therapeutic than seclusion and restraints. Where needed, a number of medicines were available; mostly, but by no means exclusively, of plant origin. Foxglove leaves for heart failure had been described by Withering in 1785, while alkaloids such as morphine, strychnine, quinine, nicotine, caffeine and atropine had been extracted and purified in the early decades of the 19th century. Potassium bromide had been used as an anticonvulsant since 1857 and in 1885 paraldehyde was described in *The Lancet* as '… a new hypnotic'. Chloral hydrate was introduced in 1869 and is still used today to treat insomnia.

At one time entertainment of the patients was deemed so important that staff (known as attendants) were recruited on the basis of their musical skills. Sir Edward Elgar's first paid job was band master at

BURNTWOOD ASYLUM, near Lichfield.—FIRST VIOLIN PLAYER WANTED. A male attendant, capable of playing first violin in the band, will shortly be required. Wages commence at £30 per year, with board, lodging, washing, and uniform after a probationary period, with an allowance of £3 10s. per annum in lieu of beer, and band pay at the rate of £4 per year. No application will be considered except from those who can play first violin.—Apply, stating age, height, previous occupation, whether married or single, giving references, and enclosing photograph, to the Medical Superintendent, Staffs. County Asylum, Burntwood, near Lichfield.

Daily Telegraph, September 9th and 11th, 1893.

6: Situation Vacant

a mental hospital in Powick, a job of which he was always proud. Entertainments were provided by local groups of amateur performers who were invited to put on shows and plays from time to time. It was not until the 1880s that an asylum band was formed.

A cottage hospital was built nearby in Coulter Lane for the care of inmates who contracted infectious diseases. Dr James Beveridge Spence, an influential medical officer, was medical superintendent from 1881 to 1924. Known as a stern taskmaster to the staff, he never wavered in showing deep concern for the welfare of his patients. Under his guardianship, the Burntwood Asylum was maintained to the highest standard. He was also integral to the development of the Medico-Psychological Association of Great Britain and Ireland, and the planning of a syllabus and examination for a formal training course for attendants and nurses.

The First World War impacted upon life at the asylum in Burntwood for two reasons. Firstly, young, fit attendants were called up to serve in the war effort. Secondly, a number of asylums were taken over by the government to be used for war casualties. There were severe shortages of food; records suggest that malnutrition may have contributed to the death of many inmates during the war. Space was required for wounded soldiers and the three Staffordshire asylums were ordered to make space for 200. It is not known how many arrived in Burntwood, but nine memorials to soldiers who died between 1917 and 1920 were placed in the asylum cemetery.

Social change affected Burntwood as elsewhere, and the asylum gradually became a hospital. New laboratories were provided where doctors could conduct research into the causes and cure of lunacy. In 1924 an operating table was purchased.

Following the First World War, and generated primarily by the large numbers of ex-servicemen requiring after-care for shell-shock, the 1930 Mental Treatment Act enabled informal, voluntary admission. Also, local authorities were empowered to set up out-patient clinics and thus the ground was prepared for the development of community psychiatric care. The term 'asylum' was dropped to be replaced by 'mental hospital', while lunatics became 'persons of unsound mind'. The road outside the Burntwood Asylum was renamed Mental Hospital Road, which changed again in 1947 into St Matthew's Road.

By the early 1940s this mental hospital had a very high level of activity. There was a flourishing farm that provided food as well as offering work to the patients, new forms of therapy, weekly cinema shows in the hall, sports, dancing, crafts, painting and social clubs for both staff and patients. With the advent of the Second World

7: Croquet on the Lawn

War, an emergency hospital was established on the site for both military and civilian patients; part of the asylum was taken over, and new wards were built in the grounds. The first patients were 242 sick and wounded rescued from the Dunkirk beaches.

The administration was taken away from the hospital authorities and placed in the hands of Ministry of Health Emergency. In spite of the war, developments continued and new forms of therapy were introduced. A library was opened, as was a hairdressing salon. Occupational therapy was introduced as treatment for the inmates. This involved specific activities to help the patients reach their maximum level of independence. A formal nurse training school was opened in 1946. By the late 1940s, however, the term 'mental' had acquired unattractive overtones, and in 1948, following the introduction of the National Health Service, the name St Matthew's Hospital was adopted. By 1950 six of the emergency wards were exclusively used for occupational therapy.

In 1951, the commissioners' report commented positively on the Deep Insulin Unit. It was believed – wrongly – that epileptic patients never suffered schizophrenia, and thus, by inducing fits through the administration of high doses of insulin, schizophrenia could be treated. The fits were terminated by giving sugar.

ECT (electro-convulsive therapy) and leucotomy operations (the cutting of nerve fibres at the front of the brain) were performed in an admirably equipped theatre. During the early 1950s, the tranquiliser drugs were discovered; this led to dramatic changes in the wards of mental hospitals. Countless younger patients who would have remained in the hospital for many years were now successfully treated as out-patients, being admitted to hospital for brief periods only during relapses. Both the Mental Health Act 1983 and the Community Care Act 1990 gave powers to health and social

8: Student Nurses

9: Dame Anna Neagle, star of *The Lady with the Lamp*, visiting St Matthew's in 1952. She gave the lamp used in the film to the hospital.

services professionals to provide support to people with a mental illness living in the community.

In 1995, St Matthew's Hospital closed. The local District Council plan adopted in 1998 proposed that its land be used for housing development, and recorded:

The site contains a main block of some architectural merit and has mature grounds of considerable visual quality including many specimen trees, open spaces and a large chapel…It is considered important that development should retain the existing ambience and the qualities of spaciousness provided by the strength of existing open space and tree cover within the site...

The Victorians have been very harshly criticised for the treatment they afforded their mentally afflicted citizens. They have been accused of building mammoth warehouses in order to dispose of inconvenient individuals; individuals who merely refused to conform. The records of the Burntwood Asylum and personal testimony of both patients and visitors do not bear out these criticisms.

'*Physicians ought to apply themselves with more than ordinary diligence to all the arts of preserving men's lives.*'

Sir John Floyer (1649-1734)

3: Care of the Injured Miner at Hammerwich Hospital

The name Hammerwich comes from the Old English *hamor* (by a hill) and *wic* (place). It was formerly a township in the south-west corner of the parish of St Michael, Lichfield. It lay beside Watling Street, which formed the whole of its southern boundary, and as a district remains largely rural.

This high place overlooking the Roman road of Watling Street has had an eventful past for such a small village, which continues to unfold with the recent discovery of the Staffordshire Hoard. It lies on the edge of the Royal Forest known as Cannock Chase, and its early history probably revolved around small groups of charcoal burners on the edge of the forest. Agriculture took over through the Middle Ages and several large estates had interests in the area. In 1851 there were 270 people in the parish, almost all employed in agriculture. The only other industry seems to have been nail-making – a tradition that goes back to the early 17th century.

Early records of institutional health care reveal that in 1810 Hammerwich began subscribing one guinea to the Staffordshire

General Infirmary at Stafford and thus became entitled to recommend one in-patient a year and any number of out-patients for treatment. From 1811 to 1818 it subscribed three guineas. In 1853 Hammerwich had a sick club, attended by a surgeon from Bloxwich; its major drawback was that the patient had to travel to Walsall for attention.

Test borings for coal were made near Norton Pool in the far western corner of the parish in 1846 and in 1849 Hammerwich No.1 Colliery was sunk. Chasewater was created to serve as a feed for the Anglesey Branch Canal, which was cut to link the colliery to the Wyrley and Essington Canal. The South Staffs. Railway was also opened in 1849, and further mines were sunk in Chasetown. The opening of the Hammerwich No. 1 Pit encouraged immigration to the area, some of the new residents coming from Ireland.

The miners started to arrive at the new Cannock Chase coalfield around 1850, when deep mining was in its infancy. This was when the Marquis of Anglesey leased his mines in the Burntwood/Edial area to John Robinson McLean, who launched the Cannock Chase Colliery. This action by the Marquis opened the floodgates for others to become mine owners, and there was a dramatic increase in mining activity, with company after company opening mines throughout the district. The Industrial Revolution had truly arrived.

The increase in mining activity inevitably resulted in an increase in mining accidents and illnesses. These could have a variety of causes, including leaks of poisonous gases or explosive natural gases. There was always the risk of collapsing mine stopes (a stope is an excavation in the form of steps made by the mining of ore from steeply inclined or vertical veins), mining-induced movements or tremors, flooding, and general mechanical errors from improperly used or malfunctioning mining equipment (such as safety lamps or electrical equipment). Use of improper explosives underground could also trigger methane and coal dust explosions.

There was a pressing need to provide a local hospital to deal with the injuries resulting from such potential dangers.

A cottage hospital was opened in Hospital Road in 1882 with two five-bed wards; an isolation ward was added soon afterwards. The cost of building was met by subscription, some deducted from miners' pay at one penny per week, as the hospital was intended mainly for victims of mining accidents.

The prime movers appear to have been Robert Gordon, rector of Hammerwich, and Arthur Sopwith, general manager of the Cannock Chase Colliery Company. The hospital commemorated Mr T. B. Wright, the Birmingham manufacturer who founded Hospital Sunday in 1859. Hospital Sunday was originally funded

10: Hammerwich Hospital 1880s

by donations and subscriptions from the middle and upper classes, as a new source of funding for English voluntary hospitals in the 1800s. The idea of Hospital Sunday originated in the 1700s and involved churches and chapels setting aside for local hospitals the funds collected from a charity sermon on one Sunday a year. It involved workers donating a penny in the pound of their wages to local hospitals. In return, contributors were ensured free treatment in a voluntary hospital. Early examples include those in Walsall (1863), Manchester (1872) and Birmingham (1873).

Mr and Mrs Wright lived at Fair View in Hammerwich in the mid-1870s. As his widow she laid the foundation stone of the hospital and later left it £12,000.

The behaviour of the owners in industry was influenced by the need to increase profits for themselves and the shareholders. Opening a hospital appears to be a benevolent action for the workers' welfare, but could be interpreted as a way to increase productivity and also help to control the workforce. By having a hospital sited close to the industrial activity, the doctor's surgery could be held in the hospital building with minimal loss of worker time when minor treatment was required. The doctor, having been appointed by the firm, had a duty to his employers to ensure that workers returned to the coal-face as soon as they were fit, thus ensuring maximum productivity and reducing the number of potential malingerers. The history of the industrial hospital followed the pattern of profitability of the industry. From the end of the 19th century, it was a requirement of law that provisions were made for the accommodation, health and spiritual welfare of workers; this evolved into today's Health and Safety legislation.

During the First World War a military ward was added and between

400 and 500 wounded soldiers were treated at Hammerwich Hospital. Extensions and improvements were carried out in 1937, including a new operating theatre, and the number of beds was increased from 19 to 25. The cost was met by a bequest of £10,000 from George Hodgkins (d. 1934), a Brownhills farmer and a member for many years of Brownhills Urban District Council and Lichfield Rural District Council. Hammerwich House, on a nearby estate, was also used as a hospital from 1941, serving as an annexe of the Birmingham and Midland Hospital for Women, before being bought by Walsall Borough Council in 1945.

Before the introduction of the NHS, Hammerwich Hospital was run by a matron, a committee and chaplains. Matron lived in her own apartment, above the kitchen, housed at the rear of the hospital, and there was a caretaker's house in the grounds. A large house, sited to the left of the hospital, was lived in by caretaker John

11: Hammerwich Hospital 1930s:
committee, chaplains and staff (including Matron, third from left)

Cheshire, with his wife Joan as hospital cook, and his family for over 30 years from 1967.

A dayroom was built in 1963, which replaced the central glass structure and gave the building its characteristic bowed frontage. The hospital was modernised and refurbished over the years, but retained many charming features like original radiators, art-deco door handles and a call lamp display for the original men's, women's and children's wards.

Hammerwich Hospital remained a general hospital until the closure of the operating theatre in 1967, and it then became a hospital for the elderly. By 1981 there was accommodation for 24 patients, and there was also a physiotherapy and X-ray department. The hospital hosted diverse medical and surgical consultants who ran their out-patient clinics. This was very convenient for patient access – local GPs could gain specialist advice on the spot from these consultants if they had concerns about a particular patient.

Complementary to the hospital, the Annie Ker Gettings Memorial Home in Bridge Cross Road at Sankey's Corner, was opened in 1923 as a district nurses' home. It was named in memory of Annie Ker (d. 1920), who was matron of the cottage hospital for several years until her marriage to J. S. Gettings, a surgeon who worked at the hospital from its opening until shortly before his death in 1928. During the First World War she was commandant of a military ward at the hospital. Much of the cost of building the home was met with money raised to support the military ward and with the Burntwood and Hammerwich Parishes War Fund established in 1919 by Mrs Gettings' efforts. The home was closed around 1951; on its site is now the Number 7 Wine Bar.

Older members of the community of Hammerwich and Burntwood

recall the very quiet atmosphere, the strict matron and Dr Pooley, who was a much-loved local doctor. He was sometimes assisted in the theatre by his wife who was an anaesthetist. Many of the photographs, wall plaques and memorials housed in Hammerwich Hospital have been preserved and replaced on the walls of the Samuel Johnson Hospital in Lichfield. The Friends of Hammerwich Hospital had a long and proud legacy of support of their community hospital, and made a generous contribution to the funds that equipped the new community hospital in Lichfield.

> ❛ Health and cheerfulness naturally
> beget each other. ❜
>
> Joseph Addison (1672-1719)

4: Victoria Hospital
In Celebration of a Monarch

In 1887 plans were made to open a small establishment for the purpose of providing health care for the people of Lichfield. One thousand pounds, the residue of the City's fund for Queen Victoria's Jubilee celebrations, was given for the stipulated purpose of providing a Lichfield hospital, and during the next 10 years donations were received from many sources. The Jubilee Fund Committee made another donation and the idea of a hospital took tangible form when the committee chairman, John Taylor, decided 'it was reasonable to suppose that a Nursing Home could be established'. In 1898, Mary Slater of Haywood House, Bore Street, a Lichfield woman known for her charity and good works, gave the residue of her estate to the Lichfield Nursing Association. This produced a substantial yearly income of £200. In addition it enabled purchase of 15 Sandford Street where Lichfield Victoria Private Nursing Home was opened on 24 July 1899 – a local memorial to the long and glorious reign of Queen Victoria.

The Lichfield Nursing Association, formerly Lichfield Diocesan

12: The original Victoria Hospital, Sandford Street

13: Plaque from the original Victoria Hospital, Sandford Street.
Lady Swinfen Broun worked tirelessly in support of the hospital.

Nursing Association, had evolved in the 1860s from the concern of senior clergymen who realised the need of the poor for some form of public health care. History suggests that party disputes between evangelicals and followers of the Oxford Movement may have affected the development of nursing in the 19th century. Leading evangelicals in Derby campaigned against the idea of nurses belonging to a 'sisterhood'. This resulted in two rival organisations being created in 1865/6, namely the Derbyshire Nursing and Sanitary Association, and the Nursing Association for the Diocese of Lichfield. Records reveal the nature and origins of the dispute within the diocese and its unsuccessful attempts to draw Florence Nightingale into this arena.

However, the stated aim of this Christian home was: 'the provision of a residence or home for a nurse or nurses for the treatment and relief of sickness of the poor persons living in the City of Lichfield or within a radius of 2 miles from Lichfield Cathedral'. It also provided an invalids' kitchen for the supply of nourishment, gratuitously or otherwise, to the sick poor within that radius. It was dependent on subscriptions and donations, the scheme for which was originated by Canon M. H. Scott, vicar of St Mary's from 1878 to 1894 and archdeacon of Stafford from 1888 until his death in 1898. One of the two wards was named after him and the other after Mary Slater. Lady Cooper performed the opening ceremony in the presence of the Mayor and the Corporation, and the Very Reverend H.E. Savage. A suitable tablet was placed over the front door. The total original cost of this home was £2,030.

An adjoining house left to the trustees by George Martin of Sandy Way, who died in 1908, was converted into nurses' quarters and offices. In 1910 the nursing home was enlarged by the addition of a third public ward, two private wards, and an operating theatre.

These extensive building alterations were made by Deacon Brothers of Lichfield at a cost of £1,377 and the home was then re-opened by Lady Cooper and re-named Lichfield Victoria Nursing Home and Cottage Hospital. Local patients were now able to receive surgical treatment in their own hospital instead of having to make the tedious journey to Birmingham.

In 1920 a fund was opened, its object being the provision of the necessary finances for the building of a new hospital and by 1932 the sum of £14,500 had been raised. A site on 'the glorious sweep of the Friary Estate' was chosen.

On behalf of his wife who was unable to attend due to illness, Colonel M. A. Swinfen Broun laid the foundation stone of the new hospital on 24 May 1932 in the presence of the Mayor and

14: Colonel Swinfen Broun laying the foundation stone

Corporation, the British Legion, other dignitaries and local schoolchildren. Made of Portland stone, this foundation stone had the Lichfield coat of arms emblazoned on the bottom left-hand corner. A metal container had been fitted into the stone and in this was placed a copy of the *Lichfield Mercury*, coins and other papers. In his opening speech, Dr T. Stuart Shaw, Chairman of the Executive Committee, welcomed visitors by saying:

> I would like first to pay tribute to all those to whom this city owes the inception of the hospital in 1887. A venture of faith we are embarking upon, the high faith that fails not by the way, faith not only in ourselves but in each other, so will this hospital be built and paid for.

'Middle class persons' were invited to put down a capital sum of £10 to insure a hospital bed, and to contribute varying sums annually to secure treatment. The 'provident working man' insured his own and his dependents' days of sickness by joining a contributory scheme.

The tender of J. R. Deacon, builder and contractor of Lichfield and Walsall, was accepted at £21,567. Built on a pleasant site 'well out of town to the South and surrounded by countryside', the hospital was described by one local gentleman as 'a London hospital in Lichfield' – praise indeed. It had been designed in such a manner that future expansion could take place, the buildings encompassing three blocks connected by a wide corridor. The administrative block faced the road; the wards faced south and west to be as far away as possible from the traffic. The theatre and out-patient department were behind the central building. The actual cost of the building and equipment would be £25,682. Material for erection came from the firm of Walter Tipper.

The Lichfield Victoria Hospital was opened on 24 June 1933 by Earl Harrowby. Furnishings were supplied by F.M. and J. Wait of Bird Street. Dr T. Stuart Shaw commented:

> This hospital, as it appears today is enough to prove that the people of this district have not forsaken their ancient charity nor changed their measure of value, for rising as it does from its ashes, it rebukes the doubter and the defeatist and asserts valiantly the spirit of service in a world distraught. This voluntary hospital has been recreated by men and women whose sole object has been the good of their neighbour.

To commemorate the opening, portraits of Colonel and Lady Swinfen Broun were hung in the main entrance hall – and today are to be found in the central lobby of the Samuel Johnson Community Hospital.

An air of lightness, comfort and efficiency surrounded the hospital

15: Opening of the Victoria Hospital – Matron Harvey (far left)

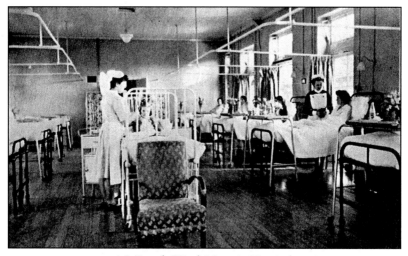

16: Female Ward, Victoria Hospital

which provided good facilities in the form of electrotherapy, ultra-violet ray and other equipment in addition to normal hospital facilities. The Vic was residence to matron and probationer nurses; other nurses had accommodation at Stowe House. Bate's Taxis provided transport to and fro.

The new hospital had a casualty department, operating theatre, pathology lab, and out-patient department. The provision of 34 beds included maternity, male, female and children's beds plus dedicated private beds – it was hoped these latter would provide an additional source of income. Patients were able to look out onto landscaped gardens from every window.

In May 1933 a welcome change occurred in the financial affairs of the hospital project, when wheels were set in motion to establish a local branch of the Birmingham Hospital Saturday Fund Contributory

17: Nurses' Sitting Room, Stowe House

Association. Previously the committee had to rely on voluntary contributions, but now a steady flow of cash was made available. Voluntary workers acted as collectors and the scheme proved highly satisfactory with Lichfield receiving from the Fund £1,300 in the first year. As £1,055 had been contributed by Lichfield members, the hospital benefited by receiving more from the scheme than had been paid into it.

Contributions were increased from 2d to 3d per week with the intention that the money raised would be for the maintenance of the hospital and to provide free treatment for employees of companies participating in the scheme, and other citizens of limited income. As a result of this venture, Lichfield gained a cheap ambulance service between the city and Birmingham.

With the new Victoria Hospital established, the former Sandford Street premises were bought by Staffordshire County Council in 1934 and re-opened as a clinic. That year the Lichfield Orthopaedic and Aftercare Clinic, a voluntary organization, moved there. Since its opening in 1923, it had occupied the house in Station Street formerly attached to the city flour mill.

In 1941 a 24-bed maternity wing was added to the Victoria Hospital. In the ensuing eight years from its opening, Lichfield citizens had worked and saved hard for their hospital – even schoolchildren had contributed by buying bricks at 2/6d each.

Under the aegis of Matron, the hospital flourished. Miss Cant joined the staff as Assistant Matron to Miss M. Harvey in 1947, and on Miss Harvey's retirement in 1948, Miss Cant was appointed Matron – a post she held until her retirement in 1973. Many changes took place under her guidance. The basement ('dungeon') was cleaned out and became the venue for many staff functions including staff balls.

Miss Cant in her time cultivated a vegetable garden, the produce making a welcome addition to the patients' diet. Jam and preserves were made in the kitchen from the harvest of hospital fruit trees. She introduced a tennis court to the grounds of the hospital. These grounds generally were kept to a very high standard; over time gifts of trees and shrubs were made in memory of those who had been cared for at the Vic. A local gentleman, Captain L.J.L. Sparke of

Langdale House, Friary Road, in a letter to the *Lichfield Mercury* of 11 May 1956 said:

> May I draw your attention to the most amazing and perfect lawn in England today – the one on the left of the drive just inside the Victoria Hospital grounds in Friary Road. I have seen many thousands of first-class lawns in all parts of the country and abroad, but nothing to compare with the efforts of the hospital gardeners. It is dead flat, faultless, looks like a velvet carpet and is the envy of every amateur gardener who sees it.

Christmas was a very special time when staff worked hard to ensure the wards embraced the festive spirit. The Comforts Fund provided gifts for each patient, the doctors would bring their families to greet

18: Christmas – Miss Cant by the Christmas Tree

the patients – one would stay to carve the turkey, and the nurses were allowed some time to celebrate the festival.

The NHS Act of 1948 wrought changes in the hospital's administration, but Lichfield citizens, through the auspices of the Red Cross, the League of Friends and Comforts Fund, remained active in raising money for new buildings, equipment and amenities for patients. To celebrate the 21st anniversary of the hospital's opening, it was proposed that funds be raised to build a patients' day room. The site chosen for the self-contained unit was the land adjoining the south-west side of the corridor leading to the maternity wing. Subscribers were invited to buy bricks at £1 each; their initials would then be cut into the side of the brick(s) they purchased for use in building the unit. On the opening of a garden fête in 1954, held to further the fund-raising of the proposed day room, Alderman F. Garrett (Chairman of the General Committee 1926-48) stated: 'In this year Lichfield has set a challenge to the rest of the country in re-asserting that despite the National Health Service Act of 1948, the care of the sick and ill is basically a personal and not a State concern'. The day room was officially opened by the Countess of Shrewsbury on 28 June 1958.

Dr Vaisey designed the remarkable chair that generations of local citizens have found themselves seated upon when in need of attention in Casualty. It was built by F.M. and J. Wait, and still is in use today in the contemporary surrounds of the Minor Injury Unit in the Samuel Johnson Community Hospital.

In 1962 the maternity unit (then 21 years old) was closed for a short while for alteration and modernisation. St Michael's Hospital helped by providing maternity care until the Victoria unit was re-opened with a reduction in beds from 24 to 12. The operating theatre was extended in 1968 with the addition of a new anaesthetic room and surgeon's changing room. Local GPs who were competent anaesthetists often assisted visiting consultants and dental surgeons who delivered general surgery, community dental surgery and gynaecological services. The renal unit was added in 1978 – a much appreciated satellite for services previously centred in east Birmingham. In 1983 there were 36 general beds divided equally between male and female. Being Golden Jubilee year, hospital staff planned a calendar of monthly events to celebrate.

In the mid-1990s theatre services became limited to day case procedures and some of the Victoria Hospital theatre staff took up new work at the Sir Robert Peel Hospital in Tamworth where the more complex operations were now performed for local patients.

The change in GP contracts that enabled them to become fund-holding gatekeepers of NHS care had a positive impact, too. Traditionally the GPs have always been gatekeepers to the access of specialist care, but now they were able to influence how and where this care was delivered locally. In *Hansard* (1995) MP Michael Fabricant is quoted:

> For the first time, however, the Victoria hospital in Lichfield has a dermatology centre, a new paediatric centre, physiotherapy, an ophthalmic centre and a new surgical wing. That is all due to money following the patient: fund-holders can direct their patients to the Lichfield hospital and consultants from Wolverhampton, Birmingham and Sutton Coldfield must now come to Lichfield. Previously, patients from Lichfield had to go to those cities.

It was also about this time that public debate about the future of the Victoria and other local hospitals began. Over the ensuing decade, negotiations resulted, despite initial public concern, in the decision to provide Lichfield with a new community hospital, of which the foundations were laid in early 2005.

In fact the first brick was placed by Mr Sam Ellicott, former administrator of the local hospital for some 20 years. He has commented:

> I feel really proud to be part of the history unfolding and, at the time, I saw myself as a representative of staff of all grades. My part in the past history was only a small one in comparison to many named in the various chapters of this book.

The Victoria Hospital closed its doors for the final time in January 2007. The site of the former hospital was approved for the development of 60 homes, the landscape of which will include a memorial garden, where the foundation stone of the much-loved Victoria Hospital will be placed.

'Hope is necessary in every condition. The miseries of poverty, sickness, of captivity, would, without this comfort, be insupportable. '

Samuel Johnson (1709-1784)

5: St Michael's Hospital:
From Workhouse to Hospital

Leaving Lichfield by the old north-east turnpike road, now called Trent Valley Road, the traveller passes a rather sombre group of buildings, once the site of St Michael's Hospital. This hospital had a reputation as a place where patients were looked after by doctors and nurses with compassion, courtesy and kindness. It could care for about 140 patients, mainly the elderly, but it served all in need in the local community.

The old bricks of the original building could relate a very different story of its origins.

The English Poor Law of 1601 marked the beginning of state-provided relief for the poor. Although it made no mention of workhouses, it did place a legal responsibility on each parish to care for those within its boundaries who, either because of age or infirmity, were unable to work. The Act proposed the construction of housing for the impotent poor, who included the elderly and chronically sick, but most assistance for the poor continued to be

19: St Michael's Hospital

in the form of outdoor relief – money, food, or other necessities given to those living in their own homes, funded by a local tax on the property of the wealthiest in the parish. The workhouse system began to evolve in the 17th century as a way for parishes to reduce the cost to ratepayers of providing poor relief. The Workhouse Test Act of 1723 was introduced to prevent irresponsible claims on a parish's poor rate. Anyone seeking poor relief could be obliged to enter a workhouse and undertake a set amount of work, usually for no pay, a system known as indoor relief. Many parishes established workhouses during the 18th century, and by the 1830s most parishes had at least one. The Elizabethan Poor Laws were abolished in 1834 and replaced by new legislation: The Poor Law Amendment Act. This Act was to be revised many times during the 19th century.

In the early part of the 19th century, there were three workhouses in Lichfield, each belonging to a parish church – St Chad's in Stowe

Street, St Mary's in Sandford Street, and St Michael's on Greenhill.

A meeting of the Workhouse Board of Guardians was held on 22 December 1836 and Edward Grove Esq. was appointed Chairman. Other appointments included Rev. William Gresley as Vice Chairman; Phillip Dyott as Clerk to the Board of Governors; two relieving officers at salaries of £100 p.a. each; and John Hewitt as Medical Relief Officer at a salary of £50 p.a. This new board met again on 3 February 1837 during which the plan to create a new Lichfield Union Workhouse was founded.

Henry Gray was appointed as the first Registrar of Births and Deaths.

At the next meeting held on 9 March 1837, it was decided to place an advertisement in the *Staffordshire Advertiser*, the *Birmingham Herald* and the *Wolverhampton Chronicles* for 'Plans and Specifications for a Workhouse to hold two hundred paupers, in accordance with Mr. Kempthorne's Model' (contained in the second report of the Poor Law Commissioners).

On 20 April 1838 the board decided that the present workhouse accommodation should be used for the purposes of the Union for a further 12 months. However, a few weeks later on 1 June 1838, a committee was appointed to take steps to carry into effect the resolution of the board to build a new workhouse, namely 'that the site nearly opposite Greenhill Churchyard is recommended for this new workhouse'.

A piece of ground opposite St Michael's Church was purchased from Lichfield Corporation, at a price of £200 per acre, and land adjoining this was purchased from Lord Lichfield, also for £200 per acre.

The plans produced by Scott and Moffatt, Architects, London, were

20: St Michael's Hospital 1838

chosen (Sir Gilbert Scott became a very well known architect and was later responsible for major repairs to Lichfield Cathedral). On 24 May 1838 building commenced with Mr Grove, the Chairman, laying the first stone. During the same year Queen Victoria was crowned and on 13 July 1838 an allowance of £5.18s.11d was made for appropriate celebrations for the paupers.

Mr William Sissons of Hull carried out the building at a cost of £2,939. The specifications stipulated 'bricks to be made from clay dug from foundations'. The only bricks purchased were the blue bricks used in the diaper decoration to be seen on the front and sides of the main buildings.

Two years later, on 8 May 1840, the Union Workhouse opened its doors, able-bodied paupers having been employed in its erection.

The workhouse comprised two substantial buildings. The entrance to the principal building was through a two-storey archway (now under a preservation order). On either side of this archway were single-storey wings, the one to the north-east housing a chapel, and the one to the south-west containing the boardroom and offices. The archway was gated and the whole of the institution and land was enclosed behind a brick wall surmounted at intervals by spikes. The windows were distinctive, being fashioned with mullions and transoms.

Through the archway and across the courtyard stood the other main building. Again the same pattern was followed, but this time with two-storey wings flanking a three-storey central building, which was the Master's domain. The front door of the Master's house had a stone porch, and an ornamental cupola occupied the centre of the roof. The wings of the house provided accommodation on one side for females and on the other for males, both sexes being firmly segregated by the Master's house and dividing walls across the courtyard. A single-storey dining hall was sited at the rear of the Master's house and the whole building had many gables, typical of building at that time. A new block ('D') was erected north-east of the main building in 1841.

It is assumed that the buildings were built over the foundations of the old parish workhouse, but no written evidence has been found to substantiate this.

The paupers had to work hard, rising at 5.45 a.m. They worked from 7 a.m. until 12 noon, followed by an hour's break. Work started again at 1 p.m. and finished for the day at 6 p.m. Bedtime was at the early hour of 8 p.m. The men picked oakum and broke stones, whilst the women carried out work appropriate to their physical capacity; e.g. cleaning the workhouse, caring for children and sewing, particularly the uniforms of grey cloth made for able-bodied male inmates.

The main constituent of the workhouse diet was bread. At breakfast it was supplemented by gruel or porridge – both made from water and oatmeal (or occasionally a mixture of flour and oatmeal). Workhouse broth was usually made from the water used for boiling the dinner meat, perhaps with a few onions or turnips added. Tea – often without milk – was provided for the aged and infirm at breakfast, together with a small amount of butter. Supper was usually similar to breakfast.

The mid-day dinner was the meal that varied most, although on several days a week this could just be bread and cheese. Other dinner fare included:

- pudding — either rice-pudding or steamed suet pudding. These would be served plain. In later years, suet pudding might be served with gravy, or sultanas added to make plum pudding, particularly when served to children or the infirm.

- meat and potatoes — the potatoes might be grown in the workhouse's own garden; the meat was usually cheap cuts of beef or mutton, with occasional pork or bacon. Meat was usually boiled, although by the 1880s, some workhouses served roast meat. There was some scope for local variation; for example, some unions in Cornwall were allowed to substitute fish for meat. From 1883, all workhouses could if they wished serve a fish dinner once a week.

- soup — this would usually be broth, with a few vegetables added and thickened with barley, rice or oatmeal.

Although healthy in some respects – for example, sugar was rare until the 1870s – the workhouse diet was often created from the cheapest ingredients. Milk was often diluted with water. Fruit was rarely included.

Adequate, though spartan, sanitary arrangements were made, night closets being provided. However, these closets were locked first thing in the morning and opened late at night by the Master or Guardian.

The female paupers had one toilet in their wing and another by the entrance gate to the hospital. This outside toilet had no door and no privacy was offered. When the women needed a bath they had to go outside their own wing and behind the Master's house to the end of the male wing where a bathroom had been provided. It was stipulated that all the patients should be kept clean and provided with a change of clothing once each week.

In spite of these rigorous conditions, paupers were probably much better off within the province of the workhouse than those people living in the hovels in the city and surrounding villages who had no conveniences and little, or very meagre, financial means. The workhouse paupers were provided with food, warmth and shelter.

Workhouses were known by the name 'The Spike' and many reasons were given for this. The spikes on top of the walls indicated to tramps the fact that they could obtain overnight sleeping accommodation there. Also, the distinctive roof could be seen from a distance and tramps could plan their day's walk accordingly. It is also said that tramps slept with their arms supported by a rope attached to spikes. This rope was released at a certain time early in the morning and if the tramps were not already awake they were very abruptly woken up.

The Public Health Act of 1872 brought more changes and on 8 August 1872, proposed plans for casual wards were forwarded to the Local Government Authority by Mr Hacker, Architect. Many workhouses had a significant transient population, being under obligation to provide for anyone who applied. These wards appear

21: Mid-day Meal Ticket

to have provided shelter for many others, including those 'tramping poor' searching for seasonal work, although it is difficult to know exactly how the casual wards were used, or when and how often an individual or family entered a workhouse. In these casual wards vagrants were housed separately from longer-term residents as they were deemed to be the most work shy and had, it was feared, a potential for violence and criminal behaviour, and the potential to corrupt the deserving poor. Tramps were given meal tickets for the main meal of the day. This provided a very meagre diet.

The plans for casual wards were approved, and then postponed. On 27 December 1872 the Guardians were instructed to erect the wards and on 20 June 1873 the Local Government Board sanctioned the expenditure of £634 for this purpose.

The builder, Mr Daker, completed the erection of the wards on 8 January 1874 and a married couple were employed at salaries of £20 and £15 per annum to take charge. Furniture cost no more than the stipulated £20.

Eighteen years later, in 1892 an infirmary was erected. This building, later known as 'A' Block, had four female wards. The institution was again enlarged by the erection of a dining hall and kitchens in 1893, more casual wards in 1901 and infirm wards and a nursery in 1908.

The institution was self-sufficient, all vegetables being home grown. Pigs were kept in sties at the north side of the grounds. During the late 1930s pig-keeping proved to be a profitable sideline for the institution, and in August 1936 six pigs were sold for £33. Five wells were sited in the hospital grounds and these helped to make the hospital completely independent.

Inflation existed even in the early 20th century. On 8 October 1909, the committee advertised for a married couple at salaries of £25 and £20 per annum (an increase of £5 over 35 years): 'The master to perform the duties of Labour Master, Tramp Master and Male Attendant for the Infirm Wards, and the wife to act as female attendant…The baker to continue to assist.'

The Case Paper System was introduced on 8 March 1912. This meant that information about the patients was kept in folders in an office and was not open to display at the foot of each bed. A clerk was allowed the sum of £50 for a period of 12 months, to bring this system into proper working order. During the same year the entrance to the workhouse was improved by asphalting, at a cost not to exceed £3.

It was proposed that separate house committees be appointed and reports made regularly by the principal officers to the committee. The house committee would oversee recruitment of staff, admission of inmates and other administrative duties that ensured the functioning and accountability of the institution.

On 21 May 1920 a plot of land at the rear of the institution, consisting of one acre and twenty perches, was purchased from the Ecclesiastical Commissioners for £185. Leasehold cost a further £30. It is understood that this land was later sold for a nominal sum and Rocklands School erected on the site.

The average per annum cost for the poor previous to 1836 under the Overseer's Administration was £7,985. Seventeen years later in 1853 under the Guardian's Administration the cost had dropped to £4,113. By 1929 however, under the Guardian's Administration the cost had risen to £31,228. This figure did include the care of 'lunatics' at £6,636.

The Local Government Act 1929 made changes to poor law and local government in England and Wales. It abolished the system of poor law unions in England and Wales and their boards of guardians, passing their powers to local authorities. It also gave county councils increased powers over highways, and made provisions for the restructuring of urban and rural districts as more efficient local government areas. Workhouses became public assistance institutions.

Mr and Mrs Standing took office as Master and Matron on 14 September 1936. Later that year, mass unemployment and extreme poverty in the north-east of England drove 200 men to march in protest from Jarrow to London. Their MP, Ellen Wilkinson ('Red Ellen') was with them as they came south to petition Parliament. On 28 October, the workhouse catered for these 'Hunger Marchers'. They were fed, provided with shelter and given medical care by the staff of the institution.

Improvements were made to the buildings: a Pastors' Lodge was installed, the high dividing walls at the front entrance were reduced by two feet in height, a glass veranda was added to the Nursery Block and the 'Tramp Ward' was converted into a nurses' home.

In 1937 Mr Standing recommended to the Board of Governors that male patients over 60 should be allowed 'leave of absence' each evening during the summer months between the hours of 6 and 8. This was indeed a step forward and marked the beginning of far more humanitarian treatment of the inmates. At this time four mentally ill patients were being cared for by the staff, and the top floor of 'A' Block still served as a maternity unit. The bath attendant/barber received the munificent sum of £2.15.0d per week.

At the outbreak of war on 3 September 1939, the staff of the institution were made responsible for their own air raid precautions, fire fighting and civil defence. The old buildings provided shelter for 137 servicemen who were housed in the infirm block as well as in the actual hospital. These patients were not war casualties, but victims of influenza, laryngitis, bronchitis and pneumonia. Though many were seriously ill, there were no deaths and they were all discharged by May 1940.

The workhouse became an emergency hospital and in the latter part of 1940 admitted 193 evacuees from Yarmouth. Twelve died and 82 were discharged; the remainder stayed in the hospital. They also received 70 evacuees from London. It is difficult to envisage the problems associated with caring for so many additional people and one wonders how they were all accommodated.

Pigs were still being reared, but had to be sold to the Ministry of Food, from whom permission had to be obtained before two pigs could be killed in order to provide the hospital Christmas dinners.

A change in administrative strategy was necessary in order to reflect the changes in society which had gradually taken place since the Poor Law Act of 1834. Previously the workhouse had been regarded as a charity, paid for by the privileged for the benefit of the under-privileged. This role had now to be adapted to the needs of the general population, in addition to providing for the destitute members of society. This change in the role of the institution was associated with changes in health care. The following points were raised, showing a caring and forward-looking attitude to the problems of ill health, age and the financial state of the populace:

- Long term care of the elderly should not be the function of the workhouse institution, and elderly patients should not be isolated from the community.

- Specialist treatment and grouping should be taken into account when considering incapacity/age/mental capacity/temperament. It was of vital importance that elderly, mentally alert, patients should not be cared for with those suffering from senile dementia.

- There was a need for 'paying' hospital accommodation.

By October 1944 the staff situation was desperate, with over 300 beds and only 29 nursing staff on active duty (both day and night). No further patients were admitted. On the cessation of hostilities in the summer of 1945, there were 226 patients in the hospital.

The name of the hospital had been the subject of many discussions in the preceding years and in 1946 the request was again made that the name should be altered to St Michael's Hospital. However, this request was held in abeyance by the Public Assistance Officer pending the County Court's decision on a similar request by another institution.

In July 1947 the Master arranged outings for the nursery children after obtaining permission from the County Public Assistance Officer, the condition being that the hire of a pony and trap was not to exceed £20 per annum. These outings were successful and became a permanent arrangement.

Permission was then granted for adult inmates to go to the local cinema, for which complimentary tickets were provided.

In the autumn lawns were laid and a new drive completed in front of the main hospital block. The grounds were improved and canteen facilities were provided for non-resident staff and patients' visitors.

With the introduction of the National Health Service in 1948, the Poor Law institution on Greenhill became the scene for many changes. The first and most important change was that it officially became a hospital, in this case St Michael's Hospital, dedicated to the care of the sick, elderly people of Lichfield and the local villages. Despite this change of name to hospital, buildings called Part III accommodation were set apart for the able-bodied, elderly paupers.

This change was slow in getting under way and it was not until the appointment of a new Matron, Miss J. Lewis, on 1 April 1950 that

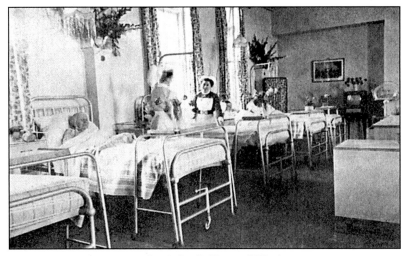

22: St Michael's Hospital Ward

any significant alteration took place. The new matron took sole charge of the hospital staff, replacing Mr and Mrs Standing, the last Master and Matron of the Poor Law institution. When Miss Lewis originally took command of the hospital there were approximately 200 patients, including children.

On her appointment Miss Lewis found that conditions at St Michael's Hospital were very poor indeed. Inadequate bedding and unbelievably cramped sleeping quarters (the beds being only an arm's length apart) were two of the many problems facing her. Before the National Health Service was started, the authority in the Poor Law institutes was paid according to the number of inmates they could accommodate.

The tramp ward still existed at the south-west entrance to the hospital; so too did the outside toilet. Both these buildings were demolished in the early 1950s. The punishment cells where refractory male paupers were held were abolished. These cells had peepholes in the doors to enable close observation to be kept on the occupant.

'A' Block had no day room and the balconies were open to the elements. The Comfort Fund provided the money for glazing the balconies and also a day room.

Central heating replaced the old black stoves which were a familiar feature of the old institution, being sited in the centre of each ward with pipes running the length of the ward beneath the floor. 'A' Block provided accommodation for 101 patients and a further 10 children were living on the third floor.

'B' Block was the maternity wing providing 25 beds. This unit transferred to the Victoria Hospital on 1 September 1961, thereby leaving 'B' Block partly vacant to house the male ward on the ground floor and the female ward on the first floor.

'C' Block was originally a children's home. When the children were moved to the Poplars, the unit was utilised as a chest unit, the patients being under the care of Dr Herszenhorn and Dr J. Elsom. This closed on 14 November 1970 and the building then became a home for a small number of young chronically sick patients.

The building at the end of the original male wing of the institution was opened as a day hospital in February 1965. Before this date it provided the Part III accommodation for 24 males, the other wing providing similar accommodation for 24 females.

The wards were visited regularly by the Hospital Management Committee (two members being Mrs Griffiths and Mr Halfpenny, who was once Mayor of Lichfield). This committee held their meetings in the St Michael's Hospital boardroom. Group Headquarters eventually moved their offices to Good Hope General Hospital in 1966.

Miss Lewis had intended staying for one year only, but stayed 20, retiring on 30 April 1970. Miss Lewis was aided by two clerks only, and conditions very slowly improved for both patients and staff.

The new day hospital was then opened in the old nurses' home in September 1973. Provision was made at the hospital for various specialised clinics as well as physiotherapy treatment and occupational therapy. For a time, St Michael's Hospital played a part in the training of State Enrolled Nurses; however, it ceased to do so at the beginning of the 1980s.

In this time of change and improvement the wells were covered and many beautiful trees were felled. Progress can seem very ruthless at times.

St Michael's provided accommodation for a maximum of 140 patients and had a competent staff of caring nurses, both trained and semi-trained. At this time the administrative team had increased its numbers from the original two clerks and was headed by the Sector Administrator, Mr Sam Ellicott, who joined St Michael's Hospital in June 1975.

Mr Ellicott was responsible for the administration of no less than five hospitals with a distance between them of approximately 18 miles:

- St Editha's Hospital, Tamworth
- Tamworth General Hospital
- St Michael's Hospital, Lichfield
- Victoria Hospital, Lichfield
- Hammerwich Cottage Hospital

During the summer of 1977, 'C' Block was temporarily closed for three months due to staff shortages. Conditions on the block were also upgraded. Members of the general public, the hospital staff, and Lichfield Round Table No. 250 combined to present the hospital with a specially adapted minibus. This marvellous gift allowed patients to venture out on trips to various local places of interest and certainly added colour to their lives. The hospital in this instance was ably supported by a team of voluntary drivers who offered their services to drive the minibus.

1977 also witnessed the first Open Day for many years. This proved quite a successful undertaking although the visitors were smaller in number than anticipated.

The hospital was very fortunate in the support it received from many voluntary organisations including:

- Lichfield Civic Society
- The Comforts Fund
- The Good Companions
- Lichfield Round Table
- The Lion Club of Sutton Coldfield
- The New League of Friends
- Red Cross and St John Ambulance Brigade
- Rotary Club of Sutton Coldfield
- Women's Royal Voluntary Service (WRVS)

The Comforts Fund provided wine to celebrate the Royal Wedding of Prince Charles and Lady Diana on the 29th July 1981 and the Hospital Social Club arranged social evenings on 'D' Block and the other wards. 'D' Block was subsequently renamed 'David Parry

Ward' after the late Dr David Parry, Consultant Physician, who had a special interest in geriatric medicine, and who looked after patients at St Michael's Hospital after the retirement of Dr Johnson. Dr Parry died suddenly in December 1979.

Through the 1990s and to the present day, one of the most important functions of the hospitals on this site is rehabilitation of older people after episodes of illness which threaten to constrain their lives. This is in line with the NHS Community Care Act (1990) and new initiatives in the management of compromised health in older people. There is emphasis on teamwork with all disciplines contributing to the care plan of the individual. This aims to enable continuing independence, with support, at home for as long as possible.

In the mid-1990s most of the hospital's functions were transferred to the Victoria Hospital, leaving only the physiotherapy and occupational therapy on site.

Today the Staffordshire and Shropshire NHS Foundation Trust provides mental health services in the listed buildings of the former workhouse. On the main hospital site stands the new Samuel Johnson Community Hospital, opened by Her Royal Highness, The Princess Royal, in January 2007.

❛ A physician can sometimes parry the scythe of death, but has no power over the sand in the hourglass. ❜

Hester Thrale (1741-1821)

6: Hospital Staff and Volunteers

Our story so far has told the evolution of the institutions and buildings in which both acute and restorative health care has been provided over the past two centuries for the citizens of Lichfield and surrounding villages. Though each building has left its imprint on the communal memory, it is the humane and professional care given within its walls that has resulted in the improvement of health and well-being of the population from cradle to grave.

This chapter does not represent a formal history so much as a narrative and anecdotal account of hospital staff and many others who brought the hospitals to life, and life to the hospitals.

Nurses

In 1865 Florence Nightingale was engaged in the training of nurses and influencing Parliamentarians on the improvement of public health and the building of hospitals. She was approached by Anglican clergymen from Lichfield who, aware of the health needs of the local people, were seeking to establish a Diocesan Nursing Association to provide trained nurses to meet the needs of both rich and poor. Though she refused to be drawn into ecclesiastical disputes that were prevalent at the time, she did help by providing a Superintendent of Nursing and four trained nurses from St Thomas' Hospital, who served both the Lichfield and Derby Nursing Associations. Probationer nurses from the Lichfield Association were sent to the Royal Hospital, Wolverhampton to undertake training during the late 1860s. The Lichfield Diocesan Nursing Association, whose centres of activity were mainly Wolverhampton and Stoke-on-Trent, had no large hospital equivalent to the already established Derby General Infirmary, nor the wealthy patronage of the Derby Nursing Association. Due to these factors, its finances were no longer sustainable by 1871 and it ceased to exist. It was superseded by the Staffordshire Institution for Nurses founded by Bishop Stamer of Stoke-on-Trent in 1872.

At the opening of the Lichfield Victoria Home for Nurses in Sandford Street in 1899, Mr S. Lipscomb Seckham, a generous benefactor, reminded the gathered audience:

> We have not attempted to establish a Hospital or a Convalescent Home...our objective has been to establish in a convenient locality on a substantial basis a Home for Nurses, who will devote the whole of their time free of charge to the relief and comfort of our poorer citizens who are in trouble, sickness or distress, and by the aid of a good Invalid Kitchen, supply them with such creature comforts that often when most needed are not within the reach of the poor. We have also...supplied a long-felt want in this City, namely temporary accommodation to sufferers of accident...who would not now be obliged to travel to Walsall or Hammerwich, or be placed in the Workhouse Infirmary.

Nurse Harding was thanked for having charmingly decorated the entrance with flowers for this occasion. The reader may deduce that there was only one nurse, because during the opening speeches, Mr J. Fowler, speaking on behalf of the Executive Committee, stated that it was 'evident that they would soon require the services of a second nurse, as in connection with the case from Elmhurst, the nurse was up nearly all night'.

A poignant tale is recounted by Mr R.A. Gilbert, who recalls a piece of his own family history:

> My great aunt Miss Edith Gilbert was matron of the Victoria Home for Nurses, when tragedy altered her pathway. Her brother Arthur and his wife Emma were parents of three young boys. Emma died in November 1899 after giving birth to her youngest child Percy (my father) at the age of 34. Sadly, Arthur died, aged 37, six weeks after losing Emma. Matron Gilbert stepped into the breach and became their official guardian, having some years later to sacrifice her career to do so. She died in 1962, aged 92, having outlived all her 'boys' by some 10 years. Had this tragedy not occurred Matron Gilbert could have been the first matron of the new Victoria Hospital...

A few years earlier in 1893, Dr Spence of the Burntwood Asylum, alongside his colleagues in the Medico-Psychological Association of Great Britain and Ireland, introduced examinations for the 'Certificate of Proficiency in Nursing and Attending on the Insane'. By 1895 announcements for these examinations were placed in *The Lancet*, *The Nursing Record*, *The Hospital* and the *British Medical Journal*.

Probationer nurses were resident at the Victoria Hospital from its inception in 1933, and later at Stowe House. There were limited opportunities to socialise outside the hospital walls, and fraternising with members of the opposite sex was closely monitored by Matron. One young nurse has never forgotten Matron Harvey (who had a slight speech impediment):

> We did have a Christmas party, us junior nurses with Matron Harvey. At half past ten she stood at the door to say goodnight to all of our friends, and then we could have five minutes outside, but no 'tissing or tuddling'.

Matron Harvey is remembered as a formidable, well-built, no-nonsense woman. She is credited for the exemplary manner in which she conducted her role, never asking staff to undertake work that she would not do herself. She wore her uniform with as much precision as she did her work: her dark blue dress, starched white cuffs, and cap always worn when on duty. Her belt had a well-polished silver buckle, which was worn over a spotless white apron.

One Friary school girl, Miss Theobald, had completed her nurse training at the Queen Elizabeth Hospital, Birmingham, when in the early post-war years a twist of fate led her to return to her Lichfield home. The family home was close to the Vic, making it highly suitable for her to continue her nursing career, though Miss Theobald's training school had led her to regard it as a 'tin-pot hospital'. She called into the Vic to ask to speak with the Matron, Miss Harvey, about possible job opportunities and was delighted, after a short but concise interview, to be appointed immediately to the post of Theatre Sister. Her initial delight was short-lived when she found herself to be in charge of an outdated area with limited fittings that she can recall to this day:

> A tatty white glass-topped table, white enamelled trolleys, two glass-fronted instrument cupboards hung flush to the walls...grubby white big pin-cushion with needles stuck into it, an enamel sterilising dish

containing emergency needles, gas cylinder and sterilising unit.

It was just as well there were no operations scheduled for the immediate future, as this gave the new Sister the opportunity to re-paint the trolley, polish the glass and teach herself to operate the ancient gas fired sterilising unit. Her contract involved '24 hour turns' shared with matron, which meant essentially being on call for a whole day and night and covering the Vic when emergencies arose with no recompense for unsocial hours worked. She personally paid for the installation of a telephone in her father's house so that a GP could phone her in an emergency. The night sister would light the gas-fired sterilising unit whilst Sister Theobald cycled round to the Vic. Modern technology even followed her to the Lichfield cinema, where, settling into the film one evening, her enjoyment was abruptly shattered by the words: SISTER THEOBALD... WANTED IN RECEPTION...CALL FOR YOU. There was no escaping her duties that night!

In time, funding became available to modernise the operating theatre and Sister Theobald was given the responsibility of ordering all the new equipment, enabling her to recreate a 'mini Queen Elizabeth theatre'.

Nurses cared for patients from all walks of life, and addressed whatever health need was presented to them. Angela Reynolds, Ward Sister, recounts the story of a little girl who'd been an in-patient in the female ward:

> There was a nice little girl and she really hadn't got very much. We had lots of staff with young children then...so we managed to get some clothes and we kitted her out with all types of attire. But the time came for the child to be discharged and I spoke to her parents who said, 'We'll come back and get her in the

morning, Sister, but we'll take the things now.' And guess what? They never appeared! So we had to call the police who investigated, only to discover that her family, who were travellers, had moved on and left her. Taken the clothes to sell, but left her. And they eventually found them up in Cheshire somewhere. Unbelievable!

Little Olive, a kitchen help, though petite in stature, and recalled as 'no bigger than a pennyworth of coppers', was, none the less full of imaginative endeavour. On good account, we have it that she was slender enough to climb into the main ovens in the Victoria Hospital kitchen to ensure that they were spotlessly clean.

One of the former Victoria Hospital domestics tells of an 'annual celebration' in summer when little Olive would go over the boundary at the back of the Vic and pick pounds of ripe strawberries from Maxtock Grange. However, while an unexpected strawberry tea was provided for staff and patients, for the domestics there was now an extra pile of washing up to be done.

Night Sister Ann Johnson, was also petite, but not short of personal authority and nursing skills. She was once confronted by a rather well-built, drunken, male patient, face streaked with blood, uttering profanities. Without batting an eyelid, she cleaned his wounds, stitched him up and sent him on his way.

Sister Chubb's quick thinking helped the police in the course of their duty. Many of the nurses lived in Stowe House, an elegant building, situated at the far end of Stowe Pool in Lichfield about 1.5 miles from the hospital. The nurses often used Bate's taxi firm, renowned for the drivers wearing peaked caps. One evening as Sister Chubb was due to go home from work, she and other staff on duty saw a man leaving the operating theatre, not recognised as being

23: Nurses' Sale of Work in the Victoria Hospital Dungeon 1954
Staff left to right: Sister Roberts, Vera Burbridge (Secretary), Probationer Nurse
Elizabeth Meachem, Sister Harding, Miss Toon (X-ray Department), Sister
Watson, Staff Nurse Ferguson, Sister Thomas, Mrs Harrison and Sister Wilkinson

either of the medical staff or workforce. Moments later they
discovered that a purse been taken. The hapless thief, finding
himself on the hospital forecourt presumed he could make his
escape, using the Bate's taxi that drew up. However, he had not
bargained for Sister Chubb's appearance on the scene. Much to his
dismay, she immediately followed him into the taxi, which she had
originally ordered for herself and in a no-nonsense voice directed
the cab to the police station!

Midwives at the Vic were fondly recalled by many women to whom
we spoke when gathering stories to tell this history. Twenty-first
century mothers will be familiar with light-weight digital scales for
weighing their babies. As recently as 1998, a young mother
remembers watching the midwives weigh her newborn daughter,

using the well-proven, old-fashioned 'stork' method:

> The midwife would lay the baby, without any clothes on, onto a small square towel. She would take hold of the four corners of the towel, draw them up over the baby's body and knot them together. The hook of the small hand-held weighing scale would then slip under the knotted part of the towel. The midwife could then lift the scale up with one hand, supporting the baby with her free hand, checking that the knot was secure to hold the baby. When satisfied that the baby was safe, the midwife would take away her hand. The baby was now suspended from the outstretched arm of the midwife, its weight pulling on the hook attached to the scale. The baby's weight was registered on the enamelled face of the scales, which being close to the midwife's eye, was easy for her to read. As this piece of equipment is a small device, it was especially useful to the midwife when on a home visit to a new mum and baby.

Sam Ellicott, former Hospitals Administrator, shares a poignant story:

> My own daughter, Lucy, when a student from Tamworth College, spent a period of work experience in the Maternity Unit at the Victoria Hospital. This was where she witnessed, for the very first time, a baby being born and this had a profound effect on her. Subsequently, she became a Senior Community Midwifery Sister in Nottinghamshire but died in 2003 as a result of a brain tumour.

Ann Smith came to Lichfield as a young nurse having done one of the new nursing degrees in the 1970s:

> My first post for which I was all ready and raring to go was on

the general ward under the wonderful care of Angela Reynolds...I was soon put right...Sorted out and brought down to reality! I worked on the general ward of the Vic and have been back to the Vic since and worked in out-patients and am still working, but now it's a very different story. It was a wonderful time, fantastic learning opportunity, absolutely. It was wonderful care that we received and that we gave also.

For many years the Casualty Department at the Vic was manned out-of-hours by staff nurses from the ward. Sister Reynolds recalls:

There was a man who came to us on an ambulance stretcher and what he'd actually got was a small bullet hole in his chest, but he was obviously expiring pretty quickly as he was getting greyer and greyer and more limp.

When we eased him forward, it was quite amazing because he had got a hole like half a football in his back. It had gone in and blasted out inside him causing this great hole. It really was good exciting stuff for Lichfield and after stabilising his condition, he went on to one of the bigger units elsewhere and did survive.

Sisters Jan Riddle and Chris Hickinbotham ('Hicky') managed the Vic Casualty over several decades during which they straightened many a bent limb, cleaned and closed a great variety of wounds, and taught casualty skills to new nurses and doctors.

Their efficiency, courtesy and care were valued by many; it was not unknown for patients to travel many miles to Lichfield for the initial assessment of their injuries because they knew that they would receive speedy, effective attention at the Vic.

The famous Chair from Victoria Hospital, on which children who

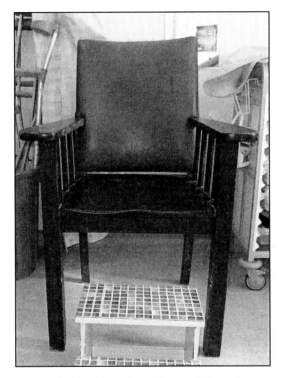

24: 'The Chair' from Victoria Hospital

are now grandparents have been treated in Casualty, continues its sterling service in the Minor Injury Unit of the new community hospital. It has been re-upholstered many times down the years, most recently due to the generosity of local firm Showell and Etheridge.

Doctors

In the days before the National Health Service, it was commonplace for General Practitioners to work alongside specialists in many hospitals. With the advent of the Health Service, GPs largely gave up that privilege and specialists agreed to see only patients referred to them by GPs. There remained, however, a small number of Cottage Hospitals, later known as General Practitioner Hospitals, and now known as Community Hospitals, where GPs continued to provide much of the care to in-patients. There are now nearly 400 such hospitals in England and Wales, which have proved valuable in attracting GPs of high calibre who enjoy the opportunity to maintain this part of their skills. Nowhere is this more evident than in Lichfield and District which enjoys continuing success in recruiting quality General Practitioners.

The Westgate Practice started as a one-man band run by Dr L.S. Tomkys from a cottage near the west gate of the cathedral in 1901. This pretty building still stands opposite the entrance to the Cathedral Close. In 1934, shortly after the Victoria Hospital opened its doors, the first General Practitioners were Dr Thomas D. Stuart Shaw and Dr R. E. Johnson.

John Thompson, present chairman of the Lichfield Civic Society, highlighted the obituary of Dr T.D. Stuart Shaw published in the *British Medical Journal* (February 1960):

> His devotion to his local hospital was outstanding, and it was indeed largely due to his initiative and enthusiasm that the present Victoria Hospital, Lichfield was built by public subscription in 1933. He also supplied much of the drive that achieved the completion of an added maternity unit a few weeks before the outbreak of the Second World War. He served this hospital well as Chairman of its executive committee right up to the time of his retirement at the end of 1945.

Dr Davidson joined the partnership in 1935, and the practice moved to the ground floor of his home in Dam Street. During the war years Dr G. Davidson and Dr A. W. Vaisey did anaesthesia for GP surgeon and obstetrician, Dr Eric Marshall. In addition, Dr Vaisey, with Dr Davidson anaesthetising, used to spend an afternoon a week removing tonsils and adenoids. He arrived on the ward one Saturday morning, requesting a bed by lunchtime for his daughter so that he could remove her tonsils and adenoids that afternoon! One could only imagine the repercussions this would have today.

Dr Ted Saunsbury and Dr Raymond Elsom arrived immediately after the war and both these doctors used to do tonsillectomies in the Victoria Hospital. They were joined by Dr Mollie Brown who came from paediatric practice in Canada in 1957. She was the first female Principal General Practitioner in Lichfield and was the only woman GP for many years. Dr Brown is the oldest surviving Victoria General Practitioner and is still active in her retirement in Lichfield.

Other characters of the early days included Dr John Gordon Brown (all other Doctor Browns have had to have a prefix to distinguish them from Mollie). He had arrived from missionary work in North Africa to set up a new practice in the Bloomfield high-rise flats in north Lichfield in the early 1960s. There was also Dr Deryck Whitney (who later went on to work as a public health doctor) and Dr Jim Collier who had previously been a bank manager.

In 1959 the Westgate Practice moved to Redcourt House (purpose-built on Tamworth Street with a Health Service grant) and started sharing premises with Doctors Marshall and Vaisey (the Minster practice's predecessors). In 1972 a young Dr Norman Whiting

25: Lichfield General Practitioners 1970
Back row (left to right): Dr C. Lockwood, Dr Dando, Dr Mollie Brown,
Dr Jeremy Duncan-Brown, Dr N. Whiting, Dr Jones
Front row (left to right): Dr R. Elsom, Dr J. Collier, Dr A. Vaisey, Matron
Cant, Dr T. Saunsbury, Dr L. Harrington, Dr D. Whitney.

arrived from Nottingham where his practice had been disappearing around him as slums were cleared.

Dr Trefor Herbert took over from Dr Saunsbury and under his careful and enthusiastic guidance the Westgate doctors became a training practice; Dr Peter Cooper took over from Dr Elsom. In 1980 the practices moved to Greenhill Health Centre, where Dr Graham Southall joined in 1983, followed by Dr John James, then Dr Bitty Muller in 1987. Dr Clare Pilkington, having been a GP trainee in the practice, joined the team in 1989. When Dr Norman Whiting retired in 1995 (saying it would take two doctors to replace him), Drs Nicola Flanagan and Richard Walsh joined the Westgate practice.

The latter part of the 20th century was a time of camaraderie and *esprit de corps*. Doctors from the three different practices in Lichfield would meet together in the doctors' room at the Vic every day for coffee and a look at the newspaper, to swap anecdotes and discuss matters of common interest. Out of this grew the 'Bunbury Club', a dining club for the junior members of the doctors, dentists and vets in town, started by Dr Whitney and Dr Harrington. A lot of doctors in those days had worked overseas and stories were told and pranks were shared, such as would never be allowed in the modern health service: how Dr Elsom's young son drank much of the sherry at the hospital Christmas gathering; Mr Berger used the hospital X-ray machine to examine his miniature dogs; Dr Partridge poured a whole case of Dr Whitney's gin down the toilet; and Dr Duncan Brown drove his motorbike with Dr Hall's mother-in-law on pillion into the hospital main corridor. New doctors were always invited to dine with the senior partner of each of the practices. There were Christmas pantomimes and most doctors and their families would visit the wards on Christmas Day.

Major GP surgery ceased in the late 1960s with the retirement of Dr Marshall, but several GPs – Dr Lockwood, Dr Hall, Dr Hallifax and Dr Southall – continued to administer anaesthetics until shortly before surgery was centralised in Sir Robert Peel Community Hospital in Tamworth. Dr Harrington carried the obstetric torch until midwifery was eventually very properly taken over by the real experts, the midwives. Later, when the maternity unit was threatened with closure, Dr Huisman championed the cause to maintain this very valued service for Lichfield. Dr Duncan Brown was instrumental in setting up and running the Renal Dialysis Unit and all doctors were very active in the Casualty Unit. This is now called the Minor Injuries Unit and is largely run by specialist nurses.

The Victoria Hospital had always been involved in out-of-hours general practice and in this respect was decades ahead of most of the rest of the country. This service evolved into a formalised Primary Care Centre staffed by nurses and GPs, run from the Victoria Hospital, making it a splendid community health resource which was the envy of many others, who struggled with inconsistent services and large, busy A & E departments.

Whilst local General Practitioners have always provided the backbone of the medical staffing of community hospitals, they have long been fortunate to have many visiting medical consultants and their junior staff to provide expert help, particularly in the out-patient department but also, when requested, on the wards. From the 1960s to the 1980s, Dr Gibbs, Dr Parry and Dr Mills became local honorary (i.e. with no pay) ward consultants. Various surgeons did planned operations and would go out of their way to be helpful when problems occasionally arose on the wards. A visiting radiologist reported on the results of X-ray examinations and the Renal Dialysis Unit benefited from a visiting kidney specialist. All these visits fostered an easy-going familiarity between General Practitioners and specialists and created a learning environment which benefited all, not least local patients.

The Victoria Hospital started with two doctors. By 1974 there were 11 GPs in three practices in town and by 2006 there were 33 GPs in five practices in town. How many will there be in another 30 years?

The doctors, along with all the other staff, look forward to the opportunities provided by the exciting new Samuel Johnson Community Hospital. They hope to live up to the reputation of Dr Erasmus Darwin (grandfather of Charles Darwin), who was Lichfield's most famous and prodigiously talented General

Practitioner. The male ward in the new hospital is named after him.

Our research revealed the esteem with which the public regard all the GPs that have served Lichfield and district down the years. We offer the reader an insight into the stories of two in particular, Dr George Davidson and Dr Joyce Elsom, wife of Dr Raymond Elsom.

Many people who had contact with Dr Davidson speak of him with the highest regard. Whether their relationship was as a patient, colleague, friend or family, his sound advice and compassionate nature endeared him to them. He was in his late 20s when he first arrived, travelling from Scotland to Lichfield with his wife, eager to start work as a General Practitioner. He had been successful in gaining a place with an established practice, of which he was later to become a senior partner. Cynthia Schmid, a former patient, recalled:

> We were very fortunate that Dr Davidson was our family doctor. A great relationship was established and subsequently most of our medical encounters took place at home. As a child I experienced him as a committed, kind man, with gentle, cool hands and a soft Scots burr. He had a reassuring air and we were at ease in his presence. To me he was all that a Doctor should be.

He was considerate, patient, dedicated, humane, a forward-thinker and hard worker. He demonstrated a genuine sense of fairness and compassion. His daughter, Mrs R.L. Forbes, confirmed this assessment of her father and the vital role he had played in Lichfield's community. She remembers him as a father who embodied the same warmth and fairness to her, which he showed his patients.

Dr Davidson always held true to his words and followed them through, when necessary, with committed action. He was known for proffering help beyond that expected of his profession.

Cynthia Schmid continued:

> (Dr Davidson)…had a special place in my mother's heart.
> During the war, she became pregnant by her fiancé, who was
> away on active service. She was living with her parents but was
> afraid to tell them and managed to hide her pregnancy until one
> evening she went into labour. It must have meant shock and
> upheaval for all concerned. My mother gave birth to a baby boy
> but my grandmother was very upset at the 'shame of it all'. There
> was talk of having the baby given away and hushing up the whole
> affair to save the family's name. My father told me that Dr
> Davidson (who had attended the birth) at once offered to take
> her child into his own home. Grandfather intervened and
> insisted that the child should remain in the family. My mother
> never forgot the doctor's kind and generous gesture. Her little
> boy was christened David – in Dr Davidson's honour.

In the operating theatre at the Vic, Dr Davidson performed minor
operations. Like his colleagues, he was not a fully trained surgeon.
This did not deter the doctors from adding to their skills and the
patients were well informed on this matter. It was a common
situation found in most hospitals prior to the NHS. Theatre Sister
Joan Theobold remembers that Dr Davidson took size 8 gloves. Not
a particularly large hand for a man, and coupled with a delicate
touch, this aided his skills in the operating theatre. He most often
took the role of anaesthetist. One time when a thyroid operation
was nearing completion, he was heard saying in his soft Scottish
accent, 'if you come along a bit of red rubber down there, it's mine!'
It was quite usual for the assisting medical staff to hear him joking,
so those who heard him asking Sister Reeve, 'Who's the Bishop run

away with to-day?' did not worry that their Sister would take offence. With a broad grin on her face, she replied, 'Actually, my mother.' Sister Reeve fielded many a joke regarding the Bishop or the Church, for she was indeed the daughter of the then Bishop of Lichfield!

Dr Davidson's daughter, Mrs Forbes, revealed another childhood memory of her father that influenced her throughout life. Though later she understood that his driving principle had been to safeguard the confidentiality of his patients, she had been told to 'never ask questions of anything'. As a student nurse this edict resounded in her head, and she found it incredibly difficult to comply with the request of tutors who encouraged her to develop a spirit of enquiry, particularly with psychiatric patients. She required a great amount of willpower to overcome the impact of those few words of her father.

However, she passed her exams and in 1970 took a placement at the Vic where she found herself treading the same corridors that her father had once walked. For her mother, there was not just pride in her daughter's studies and achievement, but also great satisfaction knowing that her daughter would not be called upon to do the general cleaning of the doctor's surgery or hospital, as she herself had had to do. Mrs Forbes related her story with humour and believes that her father would have had no inkling of the effect his words would have on his daughter in later life.

In 1972 Dr Davidson died. His funeral, in Lichfield Cathedral, gave an opportunity for many to pay their respects, as well as openly acknowledge the important figure he had become in the medical establishment and local community. 'A man of very high stature,' was the summary of one colleague, who had worked in Dr Davidson's presence over many years.

He was a man who made no distinction between any person, no matter their politics, beliefs or social status. Neither did he make any change to his method of communication and delivery of his treatment. All persons were shown equal respect and dignity. The diversity of mourners within the congregation at his funeral was confirmation of this. He was so well respected that in the majestic setting of Lichfield Cathedral, the differences between the Church of England and the Catholic Church were put to one side and each offered memorial services in his honour.

Dr Joyce Elsom gained a double first at Cambridge University during the 1940s, when there were few women accepted onto university courses, especially if choosing the sciences. Married to one of the well-liked doctors at the Vic, she maintained her own career alongside raising her family and helping her husband.

> We moved to Lichfield in 1954 to a house on the opposite side of the road to the Vic. My husband, Dr Raymond Elsom, was in partnership with Doctors Johnson, Davidson and Saunsbury. As we lived so near he was often called over to deal with casualties – in those days road accidents were initially dealt with by GPs. There was no resident staff doctor, and sometimes it was difficult to contact a GP. During the 1970s (I think), a grateful relative gave pagers to all GPs in the area, so they could be contacted in an emergency, but they were only aware of the call and had to ring back and get instructions. Also, in the early days, the GP's house had always to have someone responsible there to take the calls. In the 60s (or late 50s), the surgeries were removed from houses into a common centre called Redcourt House, which was purpose-built by finance coming from the individual partners. In its early days the doctors' wives had to clean the waiting room – I was then the youngest so had to do it frequently. The most difficult job was

removing chewing gum from the floor – not easy!

The GPs chose the receptionists until Kay Humphries came and she was put in charge and was very efficient.

As the NHS progressed, more and more rules and regulations were produced to limit the work done at the Victoria. There was no consultant available to deal with any post-operative problems if they arose. In addition the risk of patients suing increased rapidly as time went on.

Christmas time was great, my husband usually had to go in and start carving the turkey, and our own children came with us to hand plates round. One Christmas Day, our son, then aged about six, went round all the tumblers left with small amounts of drink in them and consumed them with a disastrous result. He was sick and drowsy. He missed the excitement of the day and his Christmas dinner…!

The Matron of the day always rewarded the children with a board game, which was much valued. Miss Cant, Matron, organised the hospital very well.

While my family were growing up, I used to spend Wednesday mornings doing the blood counts. There was a back room where I was able to take my microscope and set up a little laboratory. This ceased at the end of the 50s when I went back to my proper job as a chest physician.

Dr Elsom spoke of an episode when she was a patient in the Vic recovering from a recent operation. There was not much respite for her, as she found herself coaxed from her sick-bed to interpret some laboratory specimens, because she was the only local doctor who was also a trained microbiologist.

Dr Elsom's three children were born at the Vic and it was reassuring for her, during pregnancy, to know all the staff. When it came to the birth of her second child, he was six weeks overdue. It was a relief for Dr Elsom to feel the start of her labour and she duly called for the midwife. It came as a bit of a surprise to her to find that when the midwife arrived, 'She was drunk!' Thankfully for Dr Elsom, the midwife came to her senses for a split second and cried out, 'Jeepers, I don't know what to do!' Realising Dr Elsom was in a very difficult labour, the midwife had sufficient clarity of mind to know that she was in no fit state to deal with the situation and phoned the Vic for a replacement midwife.

Her arrival brought only a brief respite to Dr Elsom's shaken confidence. The replacement midwife's experience was extensive; but she had not practiced for the last 12 years and on telling this to Dr Elsom, saw a look of horror settle on her patient's face. The 12 years spent away from midwifery, however, had not marred her quick thinking. Rubbing her hands together she said to her patient, 'You'll have to tell me what to do!'

The midwife was immediately requested to telephone for Dr Johnson. He had been a senior partner in the practice that Dr Elsom's husband had joined and had become a close friend to the family. Knowing his way to their house, having been a frequent visitor, he was soon knocking on the front door. The midwife was relieved to have the doctor arrive so quickly and immediately took him upstairs. Throughout the night, Dr Johnson sat vigilantly with Dr Elsom, giving specific orders to the midwife, ensuring that the mother-to-be was as comfortable as possible. After many hours, Dr Johnson decided it was best for Dr Elsom to go into hospital for the birth. As the Elsoms lived across the road from the Vic, the ambulance had one of its shortest journeys to make. When her son was safely delivered, Dr Elsom gave profuse thanks to the steadfast Dr Johnson, and to the inventor of the telephone. It had been a major life-saving piece of equipment in her time of need!

Cases needing emergency care were often due to road accidents. If the telephone rang and the Elsoms happened to be asleep, invariably Joyce lifted the receiver to take the call. It became a common occurrence for her to kick her husband and say, 'It's for you!' Due to the number of calls that came through to their house, from the hospital, Joyce often felt that they were regarded as the 'general dogsbody'.

The Elsoms' son, Michael, adds these recollections:

> I think that the suggestion that I drank all the sherry is probably libellous – I am sure I was assisted by my sisters!

> Miss Cant does not perhaps receive the mention she deserves. When we were children she was absolutely marvellous to us. We were expected to do a ward round every Christmas Day and there were always presents for us and the other doctors' children as well. Miss Cant no doubt ruled the hospital with a traditional matron's rod of iron, but we were mostly exempt from that.

> Father's eyesight was never outstanding and how he looked after injured soldiers in the heat of the battlefield has always been a mystery. Most significantly from the point of view of the patients in the Vic was that the GP on duty at Christmas had to carve the turkey. Father hated carving and to have to carve two turkeys strained his patience!

> As I grew up, the facilities provided kindly by the Vic were increased...First there was that rather useful dark room in the X-ray department where all my early attempts at developing and

printing were carried out after more authorised activities ceased.

Secondly, a little known facility was provided by a pair of lock-up garages next to the mortuary. One contained useful gardening equipment (including the remains of a bath chair which had been converted into a plant pot carrier and ended its days as the basis for one of my early soap boxes!). The other was in due course cleared out and a friend of mine and I used it to rebuild a 1927 Austin Seven.

I did manage to cause even further havoc as a patient than I did by failing to arrive in this world on time. I spent two months in the Vic on traction after a lamp post in West Bromwich stepped out and hit my car. Since I was privileged to be in the Seckham room, visiting hours were somewhat elastic, and on most nights were extended by the arrival (after closing time at the Queen's Head) of various of my motoring/drinking friends with reinforcements for the bottles of beer which always seemed to be littered around the room! Principal amongst these friends was Julian Ghosh whose father had been a surgeon, who used to come to the Vic and do operations there in the post-war period.

Radiographers

Many efficient radiographers have safely managed patients' exposures to X-rays and facilitated rapid diagnosis of bony injury and other pathology. Two of the receptionists, Hilary Field and Joy Tabberer, tell the following stories:

> We had a request form in one day for a chest X-ray. the form gave some clinical details including TATT. Catherine and I spent hours trying to work out what it could mean, only thinking of

medical terminology. We tried thoracic and ?? but couldn't come up with anything sensible. Later in the day I happened to see the doctor, who wrote the request form, in the corridor at the Vic. Naturally I rushed out to ask him what TATT meant. He replied, 'tired all the time'. We were trying to be too clever by half!

In the X-ray room at the Vic we had a large display of postcards which were sent by the members of the X-ray team over a number of years. They were displayed on the screen where the radiographers took the X-rays. The patients loved seeing this display and it cheered a lot of them up. They said when they found out we were going to our new site, Samuel Johnson on Trent Valley Road, that we must take it with us to continue the good cheering-up process. We did, but it has been broken in two, one in the X-ray room and one in reception. It does however give great joy and comments from all our patients who do comment very frequently on it.

During the 1990s, it was agreed that senior nurses in Casualty could be trained to request and interpret X-rays, freeing the GP from the need to oversee every patient with a broken bone. The radiologist from Burton would attend a regular session at the Victoria Hospital to provide a specialist report on every radiograph. After some weeks of the nurses writing their own request forms, the radiologist, unaware that nurses had expanded their role in this way, approached the senior radiographer, Rosie Briggs, to tell her that he was impressed by the improved quality of information on the request forms. One clinician, Sister Chris Hickenbotham, in particular stood out, but he didn't recognise the signature and asked, 'Who is this Dr Chickenbottom?'

The Red Cross

Norman and Eileen Fish worked together as Red Cross officers. Their memories give a unique insight into the support provided for the community and its hospitals:

> The Red Cross in Lichfield had a long association with the Lichfield hospitals. Sadly it has now disbanded, due to the fall in membership and economy drives at Staffordshire headquarters. During the war days of 1939-45, the Red Cross had a base at St Michael's Hospital and did nursing duties on the wards.
>
> After the war most of the voluntary work by the Red Cross was carried out at the Victoria Hospital, where volunteers worked every Sunday afternoon and sometimes during the week as instructed by the ward sisters. Duties included lifting patients, assistance with dressing, serving teas, taking round a weekly library trolley, bed bathing, etc. Among the most regular volunteers were Mrs Shirley Evans, Miss Phil Bradbury, Mrs Eileen Fish and Mrs Eileen Wilson.
>
> Nursing training for the Red Cross unit was under the tuition of Sister Chubb and, on her retirement, of Sister Reynolds, to whom a great debt is owed for the high level to which she trained us.
>
> On the occasions of doctors', nurses' and staff annual parties, we were able to look after the out-patients, maternity, men's and ladies' wards, always with a doctor and sister available if needed. We also on many occasions acted as an escort on the ambulance when patients needed treatment elsewhere.

Shirley Evans was a Red Cross auxiliary for 44 years, and still works for the Red Cross, though now in their charity shop in Chepstow. She loved her auxiliary work, feeling like one of the staff. She recalls putting in many hours during the flu epidemic of 1966 because the Vic was very short of staff. She volunteered every week on a Friday morning and Sunday afternoon at 2 to allow the ward sister to brief her nurses and also share a cup of tea with them. Shirley also regularly made cakes for the nurses. On one occasion she had baked a cake for the theatre staff only to discover that the surgeon took it home and ate it. Clearly the visiting surgeons began to appreciate her efforts, because one week she had not made a cake. This lapse caused great delight in the male ward, as the surgeon came to seek her out to ask loudly, 'Where's the cake?'

Physiotherapy

Mrs Claire Lawton recalled episodes from her work as a physiotherapist in the community hospitals:

I started work as a physiotherapist at Hammerwich Hospital in October 1947, while it was still a Coal Board hospital. I had a department, but no dedicated workspace, and only two radiant heat, infra-red lamps to work with. So I had to treat my patients in the male and female ward, with a screen around them.

At Christmas, we thought we would have a party with a cup of tea and a few small cakes, while one of the patients entertained us playing carols and old-time songs on a tin whistle!

My patients were nearly always miners who had developed arthritis or some other injury. One particular man had a painful elbow. Although I warned him to keep the towel over his elbow, as soon as my back was turned to check a patient in the other ward, he stuck his elbow right up to the lamp. When I caught him he said, 'I'll burn it out, girl!' He did – next day he had a blister on his elbow.

One day a patient turned up with a bad knee. As I was not sure if there was some swelling, I asked him to let me see his other knee for comparison. I was dismayed when he had not washed the unaffected leg and it was as black as coal.

In 1951 I started work as a physio at St Michael's Hospital. There was no department. I simply had a small room above a ward and this room seemed to have been a nursery. I had two small lamps, which the porters had to bring down to the ward when there was a patient to be treated. Sometimes confusion reigned if there was a misunderstanding or the porters were engaged elsewhere.

I worked twice in the Victoria Hospital from 1951 to 1953 part-time, while also covering St Michael's, and from 1957 to 1985 full time.

At first the physio department was in the old sunlight room, situated opposite the X-ray department and adjacent to the theatre. Eventually they gave me four cubicles to work in, divided by sliding curtains.

One afternoon, on a very hot day, we had a terrible thunderstorm, just about 2, when my afternoon patients would be on their way to hospital. An old man walked in, drenched to his skin! Even his underwear was wet. Now what could I do? To dry him out, we placed his clothes by the lamps and as I had no underwear to change him into, the only solution I could think of was to stand him inside a radiant heat cradle, turned on its side. We were all in fits of laughter and several funny comments were made. In fact, he laughed so much that Miss Cant called in to see what was happening. We were frightened what her reaction would be, but she just turned around and went on her way!

In the days before Social Services, when Christmas came, I felt so sorry for my dear old patients. Nothing would happen, no presents, no fun, sometimes no family or visitors. So I thought with a bit of ingenuity I could give them a Christmas party in the 'dungeon' (the cellar under the maternity block). We looked up our most handicapped patients, who had been treated during the last year, and sent them an invitation. To cover the cost, I made an appeal to the more able ladies for refreshments and, to the gents, I begged for a few bottles of sherry, so that we could give them a drink as they came in. That certainly lifted their spirits! We even had to bring the ambulance drivers into the plot, because some people could not get into a car and there was a flight of stairs to get down to the 'dungeon'. Everyone was most willing and helpful.

First we would get everybody comfortable and settled. We would play a few games like pass the parcel or musical chairs with hats. This would be followed by tea and a singsong or, for some, a little walk! Miss Cant, the matron, would always call in as well as one of the doctors or one of our orthopaedic consultants. This was very popular and enjoyed by all, to such an extent that sometimes the patients would approach me at the end of the party and say, 'If I'm still about next year, will you invite me again?'

Eventually, the laboratory department was added to our original room, allowing us seven cubicles, a waiting area and a very small office. Quite a posh outfit to what we had before!

On Wednesday mornings, we did an orthopaedic clinic for four alternating consultants. During one of these clinics we had a miserable old lady, who complained about low back ache. She was put into a cubicle and asked to get ready to see the consultants. When we reached her cubicle and drew the curtain, there she sat in the 'lotus position' waiting for us! We could not believe our eyes and were convinced she was fitter than all of us put together!

Administration

The smooth day-to-day running of a community hospital could not happen without the hard work of those functioning behind the front-line clinical services. Ivy Wilson, receptionist at the Vic for more than forty years was renowned for her memory with numbers – she could recount every patient's registration number. When faced with a missing file, document or piece of equipment, she would pray (usually with success) to St Anthony, the patron saint of lost things. Vera Burbridge, her colleague and friend, served as administrator from 1947 to 1984; her rich memories demonstrate how very often hospital workers would go beyond the call of duty.

Peter Burbridge, Vera's husband, flew with the Royal Air Force during the Second World War and tragically went missing in action on 22 November 1944. At this time, Vera was 22 years old and pregnant. Uncertain as to whether or not she would ever be re-united with her husband, Vera returned to Lichfield to live, as her parents were able to provide her with companionship and support.

Throughout her pregnancy, Dr Davidson monitored Vera. On her admission to the maternity wing, Vera found that Dr Davidson was present and, as he had been involved with the Burbridge family for many years, Vera was pleased he was to assist in the delivery of her baby. Vera had a safe birth and was now mother to a baby girl, who she named Susan. Dr Davidson, having assured himself that mother and baby were well, went home. However, a short time later, his rest was broken when he was recalled to assist Vera. The midwife told Dr Davidson that she needed his help because, 'she's got another one in there!' Never had Vera suspected that she was carrying twins; she was as surprised as the midwife and doctor. Within half an hour, Vera became a mother for a second time and remembers saying, 'I can't look after two!' Although shocked by the unexpected arrival of a twin baby boy, Vera felt her son to be 'very special – given as a gift for his father'. Sadly, Vera's son died when in his middle years of life, but she has enduring memories of him, and the twins' childhood.

Parents had to provide the baby's clothing and nappies. The list for one baby was: a selection of matinee jackets, two to three nighties, one dozen Turkish nappies and one dozen muslin nappies. Vera had painstakingly made the necessary garments, been given some and acquired nappies for one baby. Her worries now included how she was going to double up the number. The year being 1945, recycling was a necessity, so Vera found some old, thin, white curtains, which were perfect for both the nightgowns and the muslin nappy liners.

Dr Davidson's humane understanding of his patients' needs assisted Vera ultimately to get back into employment. Though Vera was inclined towards nursing, her mother had encouraged her to gain secretarial qualifications as a first level skill. In this capacity, Vera had worked as secretary to the Magistrates' Clerk in Lichfield.

The widow's pension Vera had been receiving lasted for only six months. By the time her twins reached the age of three, Dr Davidson suggested to Vera's mother that the distraction of work might provide a therapeutic balance to the life of a single parent.

Knowing her well-honed administrative and organisational skills from her former working life, he was instrumental in leading her to the position of general administrator at the Vic. Dr Davidson first discussed his idea with Matron Harvey, who was in charge of the staffing of the hospital. He was pleased to tell Vera his plan had been well received and Matron Harvey had kindly agreed to take Vera on as an administrator. The Vic already had family ties with Vera; her cousin had worked on the building of the hospital and on its completion in 1933, found he was one of its first patients!

Part of Vera's work was to collect the fees from patients each week. This was pre-NHS days and the fees needed careful accounting. There were three categories: private, semi-private or general status. The difference was defined by the number of beds to a ward. General status related to the open ward; semi-private was made up of two rooms each with two beds; and the private ward consisted of two single rooms. The extra charge for the private rooms not only gave privacy to the patient, but also covered the costs of additional food and other niceties. In later years, other than the main open wards, there were two categories of bed available – private (fully paid for) or amenity, where the patient simply paid for some privacy (single or two-bedded room).

Vera would visit every ward, collect the relevant fee from the patient, and duly record their names and status. On returning to her office, she would ensure that the monies were placed safely under lock and key.

Hoping to spot some potential new probationer nurses, Matron Cant asked Vera to escort her to the Friary Girls School, where she had scheduled a meeting with the headmistress, Miss Gent. Matron stressed to the headmistress that she would expect the highest calibre pupil. Miss Gent responded with a haughty, 'I want only the best for my girls, it will be the Queen Elizabeth for them. 'To which Matron Cant retorted, 'And I only accept the best for the Victoria –

good morning!' Summoning Vera, she left the meeting without further ado.

The operating theatre could sometimes be a place of drama. One day there was a frightening explosion whilst an operation was in progress. Although there was some structural damage, which caused minor injuries, thankfully, none was severe. The forensic team who did the investigation to find the cause of the explosion linked it to the nurses' nylon undies creating static electricity.

During the early years of her work at the Vic, Vera was often required to convey last minute messages, as there were no mobile phones and even landlines were rare in homes. At the end of one of her working days, Vera was asked to call at 26a Friday Acre, to inform the parents that their young son should be brought to the hospital the next day, as there was an unexpected slot for his operation. This road was not on her way home, but she felt quite at ease walking along the darkish streets. In the moonlight she opened the front door and managed to find a switch that illuminated the stairwell up to 26a. Vera made her way to the top and knocked on the door, which slowly opened. The lights went out, she heard a chain rattling and the door on the opposite side of the landing opened.

A voice asked Vera, 'What do you want?' She was frightened, but explained her reason to visit 26a. The other woman, whose voice had shaken Vera to her roots, said, 'They've done a moonlight!' Therefore, her journey had been in vain, but it was a great relief for her to find that her worst imaginings were ill-founded and that the lights were on a time switch!

Mary Gardner, Medical Secretary, when first in post, recalls Vera's good housekeeping. When Mary needed a fresh piece of carbon paper for her typewriter, she had to present the worn-out piece to Vera as evidence of her need. The used carbon paper would be held up to the light, and if unused ink were spotted, it would be returned to Mary, with the insistence that she carry on with it. Over the years, new technology enabled administrative tasks to be completed with increasing efficiency.

Grace Pickering followed on in the role of hospital administrator at the Vic with great professionalism until the mid 1990s; she is remembered with much fondness.

Supplies

A management committee was responsible for Lichfield, Tamworth and Sutton Coldfield Cottage hospitals. It had its HQ at St Michael's. During the 1950s Mr Wilkins was the group secretary. One of his recruits in 1954 was John Johnson, who was to remain in post for 26 years and whose job it was to ensure that orders for supplies were dealt with and the goods distributed. To differentiate him from Bill Johnson who was employed in the engineers' department at the same time, John was known by the nickname 'Johnson Supplies'.

On one occasion, when the Bishop of Lichfield was expected as a patient, the matron, knowing that he was a rather tall man, realised that he would need a bed longer than standard hospital issue. John was always a stickler for doing things 'by the book' and required a formal duplicated written order placed on his desk; the title 'Bishop' was immaterial to John Johnson.

During the same period, when Matron Cant was in charge of the Vic and the maternity wing of Good Hope Hospital was being developed, social events were held at the Vic in the 'dungeon' (the Vic's basement).Dances and the annual staff Christmas dinner were times when all departments were represented, of course including John Johnson. The supplies department moved to Sutton Coldfield in 1960 and John went with it, but he maintained a happy relationship with the Vic staff until he retired in 1980.

The Ambulance Service

About the beginning of 1889, the Lichfield Corporation bought a carriage for conversion into an ambulance, it being illegal to use hired vehicles for carrying infectious cases. The converted vehicle was still in use in 1893 when the medical officer of health recommended the provision of a proper ambulance. Lichfield was later included in the area served by the Rural District Council's ambulance service. A motor ambulance was bought by the rural district council in 1927 and kept at its offices in St John Street. That vehicle was replaced by a new ambulance in 1935 and a new garage was built at the council offices. In 1948 the service passed into the control of Staffordshire County Council, which used a garage at Stowe House as the ambulance station until a new station was opened in Birmingham Road in 1963.

Les Ashley, for many years a journalist for the *Lichfield Mercury*, kindly provided the following story:

> I was born in 1933 and my father worked for the Lichfield Rural District Council (LRDC). In those years Lichfield had two Councils, the City which looked after Lichfield City and the Rural which covered the rural areas of Lichfield, making it one of the larger rural councils in the country.
>
> Lichfield and District had only one ambulance which was

garaged in Frog Lane, Lichfield. The LRDC offices were in St John Street, next to Hiskins' (later Kennings) Garage. The garage was where all the motor vehicles were housed including the vans, lorries, the ambulance and stores. The ambulance was housed in a separate building adjoining; the workshop was in Frog Lane. The ambulance was treated like a baby, always cleaned and polished. During the winter there was a coke-fired stove burning to keep it warm, which the duty ambulance driver had to go and stoke up on weekends.

My memories go back to about 1937 when we had a telephone in the hall, which was like a big box. My late brother and I were forbidden to even touch the telephone. It was only to be used for incoming calls, unless father had an emergency telephone message to make and then it had to be logged and reported to the LRDC. He had to fill in a book with all of his journeys to inform the LRDC who looked after all the payments.

Our telephone number was 363, and in the 1940s we had a new telephone, a 'candlestick' model and the number changed to 2363; later we had an automatic telephone. As we grew up we were one of the few who had a telephone and were even in the local directory. How things have changed.

Vincent Andrews, who is now in his 90s, was the motor mechanic. He relates that the staff who worked at the LRDC and who were able to drive, used to go out in case there were no regular drivers and assistants to hand. They did not have uniforms but they were very neat and tidy. The only time that they had to wear a white coat was when they had an infectious case and then my father or Mr Hodson had to go. When they came back the coat was destroyed and the ambulance sterilised and fumigated.

At night there was always a duty ambulance available with a driver who worked on a rota system. My father and Mr A. Hodson used to work it in turn: one week on, one week off. If a stretcher was needed he had to telephone a duty assistant. He was on duty from 6 p.m. until 7 a.m. weekdays, and weekends from 1 p.m. Saturday until 7 a.m. Monday, so every other weekend he never went out.

Living in Birmingham Road, he had a bicycle which he kept in the shed, but when on duty he kept it in the kitchen to save time. It took him about 10 minutes to get to the ambulance station. Quite often, especially during the winter, he skidded on the ice as the roads had not been gritted and came back home with a large bruise on his leg. I do not remember him breaking any bones.

When my late brother and I were asleep at night and the telephone rang we knew that Dad was going out in the ambulance. Sometimes he was out many hours. When on duty at night Dad used to sleep in his working clothes to save time getting dressed.

He was a very quiet man, but when he got talking about his experiences before the NHS, they were very interesting. Some were quite funny, some serious. He had need to exercise midwifery skills and said he brought eight children into the world, two in the ambulance itself. He was also able to lay out a body. Local people used to come to our house and say that so-and-so had died – could he come and lay out the body?

The Queen Elizabeth Hospital in Birmingham was and still is a top Midland hospital, which he used to go to quite often. I believe he used to go to Loveday Street, which was a maternity hospital. He was once stopped by the police for driving the ambulance the wrong way down a one-way street and said to the police: 'Well, you better deliver this baby as it is due any minute.' The police gave him a full escort to the hospital.

Dad knew all the roads to the major and minor hospitals in the area, but never knew the street names, so when anyone asked the way to a hospital, he couldn't tell!

Father was exempt from the forces during the War; although he had a medical, he was in a reserved occupation. When the air raid siren sounded, he would have to go to the ambulance station. Although Lichfield escaped the bombing during the War, he was always there in case he was needed elsewhere.

All the people who drove the ambulance or acted as assistants had to be trained to the British Red Cross Society standard, for which they were paid £1 a month. They also had to take an annual examination. One year Dad failed his; he was so upset that he virtually didn't sleep for a month until he was able to retake the exam. I asked what he failed on, but he would not tell me. Mum said that he tied a granny knot on a sling for a broken arm.

Once when he was going for the ambulance on a winter's night during the War (remember there were no street lights), and just as he was turning the corner of St John's Church, a white figure appeared. Dad nearly died of fright. He fell off his bicycle and as he lay on the road a voice said: 'Hello Bill, what are you doing down there?' He was a baker at Garratt's Bakery and was going home, still wearing his bakery clothes.

After the end of Second World War, trains would arrive at Lichfield

City station with carriages full of military casualties brought from the field hospitals. The ambulances and crew would be waiting to help the injured down the long flight of steps and take them to Whittington Barracks. As the first assessment place for the needs of the individual war victim, this large training centre was ideal. Once the military doctors had completed their assessments, the patients were despatched to one of three places: Aldershawe Hall, St Matthew's Hospital or the Victoria Hospital according to their clinical needs.

The Comforts Fund

The following extracts from *Born in a Cathedral City* by Cuthbert Brown tell of his father John Samuel Brown (b. June 1879):

> Perhaps the most significant of my father's charitable endeavours was the enthusiasm and help he gave in raising funds to build the new cottage hospital in Lichfield. And, to complement it, the setting up of the hospital Comforts Fund. Tens of thousands of pounds were raised under his chairmanship.

> My father was always thinking of ways and means of raising funds for the local hospital. In the early twenties he had one such idea in the form of a Grand Penny race between the Clock Tower, then standing at the head of Bore Street, and the hospital itself, situated some 200 yards away in Sandford Street. Double white lines were to be painted along the centre of the footpaths and father challenged a local business friend, Mr W.H. Bolton, whose shop, the Bolton Warehouse Co., was situated on the route in Bird Street, as to who could reach the hospital first with pennies cajoled or otherwise from the passers-by and placed on the selected white line.

> The race was held on a Friday, market day, when the town was

reasonably full with the influx of local farmers. It had a unique appeal and went like wildfire early in the morning with the lines of pennies quickly extending along Bird Street in the direction of Sandford Street and the hospital some way along. For hours the contestants ran neck and neck and there was much joviality amongst the continual knot of spectators. Friends of one or the other came along with a larger bulk of pennies and as one surged slightly ahead a cheer would be raised. During the lunch hour the flow of coins waned. Helpers gathered up the rear guard of pennies into their blue bank bags ready for counting.

I always suspected, probably quite wrongly, some of those rear guard pennies were discreetly re-introduced after lunch to whip up further enthusiasm. In any case the race was given quite a boost during the afternoon because before tea time the line had turned Sandford Street corner and was pressing well on for the hospital. My brother and I were highly delighted because father had taken quite a lead. About this time, I learned later, one of my father's business friends came along with a huge bag of coppers and could have settled the outcome of the race there and then. He said to father, 'Where will you have them, Sam?' Now I am quite sure had the question been addressed to me I would have quickly boosted father's line and, indeed, father may well have had an inclination to do the same but, to his credit, he advised his friend to place them on his adversary's line 'to help make a race of it'. From then on until dusk the race proceeded neck and neck. But, alas, there was not to be a finish in a blaze of glory for, with it getting quite dark, the race had to be abandoned with honours even, and the pennies some yards short of the goal...

...this Hospital, or Nursing Home as it was more usually called, in Sandford Street was a former private residence adapted for medical and surgical uses and had served local needs very well over a long period of time under difficulties. Only a few years previously my sister had undergone an operation here for the removal of her tonsils and adenoids which was not, perhaps, the straightforward operation it would be today. I remember being in the street below, with my mother, looking up at the hospital windows and wondering how she was going on. Suffice to say no one need have worried because Ena came round from the anaesthetic satisfactorily and her only concern had been the noise kicked up in the street below by a steamroller scarifying the road surface.

But the hospital was in need of more space and better facilities. To replace it the Victoria Cottage Hospital was built within a stone's throw of its counterpart in the Penny Race and took advantage of the fine new wide verged roads leading up to it. There were many other money raising schemes to achieve the final amount and I remember joining in with other school children in taking money to school to buy a brick for the building.

But reverting to the Penny Race it has never occurred to me, until this moment, to wonder how many pennies were involved and a quick calculation suggests that there would be, in the two rows, some 12,000. Having in mind the time and effort spent on this project the £50 by which the hospital benefited seems, by the values of today meagre indeed...

The original Comforts Fund evolved to become the Lichfield Hospital Comforts Committee in 1948; it was a volunteer group dedicated to enhancing the comfort of patients through provision of items including toiletries and nightwear. Although the committee was forced to wind up in 2009 due to a lack of volunteers, the group donated its remaining funds to the maternity unit at the Samuel Johnson Community Hospital.

Friends of the Hospitals

From their earliest days the hospitals of Lichfield and the surrounding area have enjoyed the voluntary financial support of local people – from the 'penny a week' collections of Hammerwich to the present day. Just because there is a nationally-available health service, it does not mean that appreciation by local people of a local service is no longer appropriate.

Mr Horace Whitehouse, who died in 1979, aged 71 years, was treasurer then chairman of Hammerwich Hospital's League of Friends. He worked for over 40 years as a miner and was a coal mining union official at Number 8 pit in Wimblebury Road, Heath Hayes.

For 25 years Horace was actively involved in raising funds for equipment at Hammerwich Hospital. His last campaign was to raise £6,000 for an extended dayroom overlooking trees and lawns. The extension was named after Horace, who unfortunately died before its completion.

The Samuel Johnson Community Hospital, which opened in 2007, benefited from £40,000 donated by Hammerwich League of Friends. It has been used to fund two bays in the Darwin Ward where two plaques commemorate Cedric Daker and Ron Jones.

A further £6,500 from Hammerwich, along with funds from the League of Friends of the Victoria Hospital, was paid into the new Lichfield Hospitals' Charitable Trust (managed by the South

NURSES 9 : NIGHTIES 6

NURSES from Hammerwich Hospital must have thought that they were playing a team of patients when they turned up for a charity football match against men from the Triangle Football Club.

For the soccer players were dressed in pretty floral nighties.

But the hospital team were not deterred and went on to win the fun match, which raised £240 for charity, by 9-6.

Wolves footballer John Richards joined the 300 strong crowd in cheering both teams through a thrilling game.

Hammerwich Hospital nurses on the attack.

The fund-raising Triangle F.C. team — or is it the Wee Willie Winke . . .?

26: Nurses v Nighties: a fund-raising football match between Hammerwich nurses and Triangle Football Club

Staffordshire Foundation Trust to ensure independence from the Primary Care Trust) and is now available for the replacement and renewal of equipment.

The League of Friends of St Michael's and Victoria Hospitals, Lichfield, was originally founded in 1977 specifically to organise the fundraising to provide a Patients' Social Centre at St Michael's Hospital.

Having achieved their objective, the League of Friends continued their fundraising activities to provide some of the equipment needed for the new building: crockery, cutlery, tables, chairs, etc. A piano was donated to the Patients' Social Centre which enabled the Friends to organise sing-along evenings. There were also bingo sessions and Christmas parties, to mention just a few of the social activities. The building was well used and appreciated.

Following the closure of St Michael's Hospital, the building was temporarily used as a paediatric physiotherapy centre until this service could be relocated to the new Samuel Johnson Community Hospital. This new hospital was built on the site of the old St Michael's Hospital. The listed building fronting Trent Valley Road was preserved together with the administration building to the rear, renamed St Michael's Court, and is now used for child and adult mental health services as well as various other services.

To coincide with the opening of the new hospital in January 2007 the League of Friends became the Friends of Samuel Johnson Community Hospital, Lichfield. It remains a fundraising group of volunteers. In May 2010 in Stafford, nine of the Friends' committee were honoured with a long-service award by Attend, a national organisation.

From January 1977 to the end of December 2009 the total amount of items funded in support of all three Lichfield hospitals (Victoria Hospital, St Michael's Hospital and the Samuel Johnson Community Hospital) amounted to £134,225.

Individual departments in the hospital are able to keep sums given to them separately and to use the money for smaller items. For instance, the Renal Department has a 'patients' fund', which they can use for outings by patients; the paperweight 'bricks' left over when the Comforts Fund was dissolved remain in the Maternity Department where they are for sale.

Unavoidably, replacement of equipment is an on-going requirement. Undoubtedly, all past, current and future donors can be reassured that, just as well-loved old buildings have been demolished and replaced with modern equivalents, the important work of compassionate care continues. The opportunity for thanks to be shown in the traditional, old-fashioned way remains.

Philanthropy

In addition to the League of Friends, there are still those generous individuals who express their philanthropy privately. Unknown to anyone except the managers/staff of the day, they discover what might be needed and arrange to give an appropriate amount. Amongst these unsung donors is Jean Evans, whose cheerful sprightly figure was familiar to all the staff at the Victoria. With a knack of discovering what was needed and the willingness to provide for it, Jean will always be regarded with warmth and esteem.

Outside the new building there are benches and trees which have been donated in memory of patients and members of staff. One of the benches in the courtyard of the new community hospital was given by Jean.

John Clayton, local artist, was commissioned by Lichfield GPs to capture the Victoria Hospital in a glorious watercolour painting that hangs inside the lobby of the Samuel Johnson Community Hospital. He also provided elegant line drawings of both the Victoria and Hammerwich Hospitals before they were demolished. John has waived all copyright of these works to enable them to be freely reproduced and sold to raise funds for the new community hospital.

Community hospitals have always formed local hubs for the

provision of high-quality services, particularly for long term conditions, and are able to be uniquely patient-centred. Nurses provide round-the-clock interventions and over-arching care for patients. Clinical needs are assessed by local GPs or visiting specialist surgeons and physicians who then prescribe the individual patient's management plan. The multi-disciplinary team including radiographers, physiotherapists, occupational health therapists, dietitians, mental health nurses, midwives, and podiatrists accept referrals and play their part in effective patient care. Communications and day-to-day functioning are made possible by managers, medical secretaries, administrators, IT support workers, receptionists, records clerks, switchboard operators, cleaners, caterers, porters, estate management staff and, in the past, gardeners and seamstresses, who are and were able to provide responsive, efficient services. Volunteers have always provided invaluable service either at the front-line of patient care, or through time given to the organisations that evolved to form the Hospital Friends or the Comforts Fund. Our story would not be complete without giving them their rightful place.

27: Christmas at St Michael's Hospital

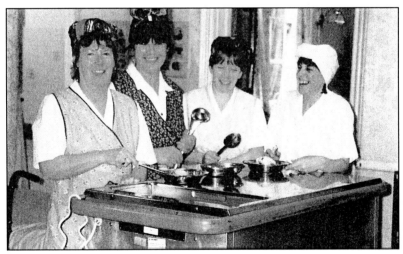

28: Kitchen staff dressed to celebrate 50 years of the NHS

'In every place, where there is any thing worthy of observation, there should be a short printed directory for strangers.'

James Boswell (1740-1795)

7: Recollections and Reflections

The original purpose of this book was to tell the stories of the patients and staff who were treated or worked at the hospitals that have served this community for more than a century. By courtesy of the local newspapers, the public were invited to contribute their stories, and anecdotes were also gathered by word of mouth. A debt of gratitude is owed to all who told their stories whether printed here or not. This chapter, through diverse voices, brings the past alive.

My great aunt Mehetable (known as Mabel), who came to Hill Ridware from Worcester as a young girl, married my great uncle Edward Grimley in 1866 at Mavesyn Ridware Church. At that time they owned eight acres of land and one cow, which Mabel managed to look after on her own after being widowed in 1894. Mabel was tiny, less than five feet tall.

In the 1901 census it was recorded that she was still living in Hill Ridware, occupation 'cow-keeper'. Yet she died in May 1909 – eight years later – in Lichfield Union Workhouse, with the recorded causes of death being senility and exhaustion.

Mabel had no children, so I guess the Union Workhouse was at least a shelter for her in her last months. I don't know how long Mabel was living in there before her death.

Mrs N. Garner

Mrs K. Greatholder recalls her school days at Wall School with great fondness. Her memories include that of buying penny stamps to fill a card of 30 – completed value 2/6d – which was given to fund the Victoria Cottage Hospital in Sandford Street. She remembers her mother paying 2d or 3d a week to participate in the 'Doctor's Scheme' – to make GP care accessible – 'all the GPs were exceedingly nice'. She faced personal tragedy with the death of a brother, aged 18, in the first Victoria Hospital. Mrs Greatholder was present when Colonel Swinfen Broun opened the Vic.

When a young girl, I had my tonsils removed. My operation took place in the Hammerwich Hospital and little did I know that I'd be working there later on in life. As for the operation all went well, though on waking up, I was a little surprised to find that there was a little boy in my bed. Sleeping soundly with his toes touching mine in the middle and our heads either end of the mattress.

Vera Burbridge

I had my first experience of the Victoria Hospital in Lichfield at the age of five years. That was 75 years ago, and like most children at that time, I went in to have my tonsils removed.

I still remember the experience of smelling the horrible gas at the start of the operation, but apparently the operation did not go well. I understand I had a haemorrhage and my stay in hospital was longer than it should have been. At that time a nurse sat with me by my bed night and day. The one I remember in particular was a lovely person, and became my hero. Her name was Nurse Gadsby.

Three years later I was there again with another common complaint – an abscess in my ear. My mother had taken me to see Dr Marshall, whose surgery was in St John Street, because of severe earache. He was so concerned that the abscess was about to burst that he took me himself to the hospital in his car. The operation took place that same evening. The one lasting memory for me was the enema I had to have. I was in hospital for three weeks and was told by a fellow patient of 10 years that there was no Father Christmas, a shattering blow.

The one wonderful experience following both these visits was the invitation to the Christmas party for each child unfortunate enough to be in hospital during the year. The wards were decorated with balloons and streamers together with a large beautifully decorated Christmas tree. We had lots to eat and a visit from Father Christmas to distribute presents to each child.

During the next few years I had a couple of experiences visiting the out-patient department for minor accidents. I do remember the Matron at that time, I think her surname was Harvey. I also remember seeing a night-staff nurse sitting at a table in the centre of the ward with a subdued light, either from a lamp or a dimmed overhead light, each night. I remember starched aprons and caps on head. Another experience I remember was a visit from a vicar when I was sitting on a bed-pan, which was very embarrassing.

My next visit was many years later at the age of 28. I was unfortunate to suffer from haemorrhoids and was advised to have them removed.

How things had changed. No horrible gas, just a prick in the back of the hand and oblivion. However, more enemas as would be expected with this type of operation. The confinement, however, was still two to three weeks.

I was at Victoria again in 1972 for a major operation. I was fortunate for it not to have been cancer, but the possibility had been there and caution prevailed. My room-mate, having had a similar operation was not and died a year or so later.

The Victoria Hospital was a wonderful place. The doctors were known to everyone living in Lichfield and we respected them. We always saw either Dr Marshall or Dr Vaisey and because my mother and dad paid into a weekly medical scheme, we were allowed to go to the front door of the doctor's house and wait in a rather sumptuous waiting room. It all sounds very snobbish, but that is how things were then. My mother's cousin Hilda Capper was on the board at the hospital, as were many of Lichfield's dignitaries.

With regards to St Michael's Hospital, I have little experience other than to say that my mother's generation always looked on it as a stigma because of it being the former work-house. However, my mother did have a short time there, following a stroke, and as she recovered she appeared to be happy there and I know she had every care and attention. My only visits were for physiotherapy following wrist operations.

I was very sad to see such a lovely building as the Victoria Hospital pulled down, but I suppose we have to go along with new technology and be thankful for the equipment in the new hospital. However, the lovely grounds and veranda, onto which the beds were wheeled on sunny days, are things I shall always remember.

Mrs M. Dale

The few memories I have of some of the hospitals in Lichfield are mainly handed down to me from my mother.

Her mother – my gran – was sent to St Michaels Hospital, where she gave birth to my mum in 1920. My gran was in service at the time and became pregnant, but was sworn to secrecy as to whom the father was, so my mother never knew who her dad was. She took that secret with her to her grave.

It wasn't a nice place to have to go to or have your baby born in. No good memories there. But I remember the workhouse, as it was known then, as a hospital. My first child was born there in 1961 under much happier circumstances.

Strict rules still applied, but we all used to laugh a lot. We were confined for ten days way back then, and weren't allowed out of bed until the fifth or sixth day after giving birth. Woe betide anyone caught out of their bed, but we had a lookout to say if the coast was clear. Also the babies were taken to the nursery at night so you had a good night's sleep. It was happy days for all of us then; so different to the story when it was the workhouse.

The memories of the Victoria were happier too for my mum who had another six children after me and my brother (during her second marriage), of which four were born in the Vic. She would tell me lots of happy stories about all the staff including midwives and doctors.

It was all so very different then.

I think the Vic was a part of everyone's life in one way or another. From being born there to passing away in some cases. I am sure most people sat in that chair. Sometimes with fear as a child wondering what was to be done to you. My own children were also treated there. But now the Vic is gone – a very sad day, and now we move on to the new Samuel Johnson and start all over again. This is a lovely hospital too.

Then we come to St Matthews. My great aunt was a psychiatric nurse for twenty years there. She used to take me to some of the many functions they organised for all the patients and staff. The patients were like family to the nurses.

I remember the garden parties. All the patients were in their finest clothes. How lovely they all looked. I was only a child but I remember thinking, Why are these people here? They looked so well. My aunt explained it all to me.

One Christmas in the 1950s, there was a competition for the best decorated ward. My aunt's ward, Edial, won third prize. So many stories she told me about her job there. She loved every day and would work overtime all the while to be with those patients, even Christmas Day.

Mrs Diane Bailey

I worked at the workhouse, about four or five years in the nursery. The matron was Matron Standing, deputy was a Miss Doughty and the lady in charge of the nursery was a Mrs Grimley. We had children from newborn to five, some were neglected or we used to have girls come in to have their babies. They used to leave them behind when they went home, some stopped with them for a time and were found work in the hospital, mostly in the laundry or kitchen. Some were fortunate – their parents took them back home.

We used to take the children out in a long pram which held about six babies. Those that could walk, walked by our side, about four of them, and we'd take it in turns to take them.

We had a porter, Mr Johnson, who kept a stables and he had a pony and trap. His daughter Margaret, or Buttons as she was called, used to come in the afternoons twice a week to take some of the children for a ride. They enjoyed that.

When we were on nights the big doorbell used to ring and one of the porters used to answer it. Often it would be a tramp wanting a bed for the night and he was taken to the 'Tramp Ward'.

We had lots of old ladies and gentlemen who used to walk about during the day and wander up town.

Sister Swan and Sister Smith were in charge of the hospital's A and B blocks. We also had a tailor to see to the clothes and sewing. Mrs Moxham brought all the children's food down from the kitchen; the children's clothes were all washed in the laundry.

The children all had a good Christmas, each receiving a present from Father Christmas. Some of the older ones used to go to 51MU, the air force station at Fradley, for a Christmas party and came home with lots of homemade toys.

Some of the luckier ones were adopted and went to good homes. Our lady in charge, Mrs Grimley, adopted a little boy when she left. I can't think of the date, but when the government took it over and renamed it St Michael's, we were moved to the children's homes now in Scotch Orchard. They had the bigger children there, but were moved on to make room for our smaller children.

We had a new Matron there but I cannot think of her name. I went down to Nurseryland in Market Square with her. We bought new prams, cots, pushchairs; we felt quite rich.

At the workhouse Matron Standing had a daughter Claire who had

29: Nurses and Children

30: Children at St Michael's Hospital

a horse. You very often saw it roaming around the grounds. I believe when she left she went to Stafford. I remember my parents (we lived in Trent Valley Road) buying a brick every week for the hospital.

Mrs D. Cashmore

My father, Mr H.T. Jackson, was head gardener at the workhouse during the war years, when the male inmates were invited or encouraged to assist in the maintenance of the then very large garden and field. Their help, in whatever capacity, within their capabilities, mental or physical, was rewarded with a bottle of Guinness and a welcome extra ounce of tobacco.

My father was generally assisted in the garden by the services of a Land Army Girl, who was from Wolverhampton originally, and whose name was Miss Ethel Knight, a very charming lass.

In those times, the workhouse, supervised by a Matron and a Master, was entirely self-supporting, with produce and fruit, etc., providing all necessary sustenance. There were two whole rows of fruit trees and, of course, the small adjoining field.

As time progressed the workhouse as such was run down, and became the hospital.

Mr H. Jackson

Sybil was 11 years old in the winter of 1940-41. One day at school she had an onset of tummy-ache, which became so severe that she could not walk and her sister had to push her home on her bike. The GP came out to see her and pronounced that she was an emergency, resulting in a prompt admission into hospital. Her case was a complex one and therefore she was greatly relieved to hear the surgeon declare that 'the Lord told me how to do the operation'. Thank goodness for that.

Whilst she was recovering from peritonitis as an in-patient in the General Hospital, Walsall, a bomb was dropped on the nearby gas works. Along with other patients from the top floor (Taylor Ward), she was moved to the women's ward in the emergency hutments at St Matthew's Hospital. It was frightening to be so ill with pain that she will never forget. Her convalescence took four to five months; all the staff were very kind.

Sybil's parents did not own a car so were unable to visit daily, but came by bus to St Matthew's when they could. The convalescence was most certainly aided by the fact that her parents brought along oranges saved up from the ration of the neighbours.

Despite the difficult times during the early war years, there were beautiful Christmas parties and celebrations with lots of food and festivity. Sybil recalls one concert during these celebrations when she sat next to a wounded soldier on the same trolley.

Sybil Edwards

My own personal memoirs of the Vic happened in 1942 when I was aged 11. Whilst on school summer holidays my friends and I were picnicking and paddling in the stream which runs through Pipe Green. Unfortunately for me, I stood on a piece of broken glass in the stream, resulting in a three-inch gash across the ball of my right foot. Having managed to hobble home, I was taken to the Victoria Hospital for treatment. After waiting a while I was attended by none other than Matron Harvey, a typical no-nonsense matron of her time. She examined my wound and decided that it would need stitching. She then proceeded, without anaesthetic of any kind, to put three stitches in my foot, which, as you can imagine, was agony.

After completing the task, she dismissed me with a curt, 'come back in two days' time and have the dressing changed'. My weekly visits to the Vic seemed to be endless, as the wound was not responding to treatment. I missed the return to school, still being pushed about in a wheelchair by my parents. At one stage, there was talk of amputation if the wound did not soon respond to the next lot of treatment. Fortunately for me everything went right and the foot healed and I returned to school, albeit five weeks late.

My other encounter with the Vic was when I was admitted with a back injury and was to be put on traction on the orders of my doctor, Dr Whiting. After spending 10 days flat on my back with a 'ton' of weights strapped to me, that hung over the bottom of the bed, I began to respond to the treatment and was allowed to get up for a short while and walk around the ward. On this particular morning Dr Whiting was doing his rounds and asked how I was. I bravely replied that I was doing OK although I knew I was not 100%.

'Right,' he said, 'let me see you walk down the ward.' I walked down the ward and back to my bed, putting on a brave face even though it was a little painful. 'Good,' said Dr Whiting, and not being a man to mince his words, turned to the Sister and said, 'Kick the bugger out, he'll be fine now.' I was discharged that same morning. What a doctor!

Mr R.A. Gilbert

During the Second World War, I was evacuated to Pipewood Camp Boarding School at Blithbury. In 1943-44, when I was 11-12 years old, I was diagnosed with scarlet fever and sent to Hammerwich. I was told that there would probably be other girls following, but as it turned out I was the only one at that time.

I remember being in a small ward with six beds and a fireplace. In the bed next to me was a girl from Cannock who happened to be the niece of one of my teachers.

The Sister or Matron used to come around every day with a tray of fruit, oranges, apples cut into quarters and hand them around.

Visitors were not allowed and my parents, who travelled from Birmingham, had to stay outside or wave to me through the windows.

However, my headmistress was allowed in, suitably gowned, and asked if there was anything I wanted. I said: 'pop and a box of paints'. I was sent some orange squash and a beautiful paint box which I did not have a chance to use. I was mortified when I was not allowed to take it away with me.

All my clothing had to be treated before I came out.

Mrs J.R. Lum

Hammerwich Cottage Hospital has quite a few memories for me. My mother had to go in during the war 1943-44, to have a hysterectomy – very serious in those days. Birmingham and Coventry were being bombed, so the doctor from Birmingham came to Hammerwich to perform the operation. It was so serious that she was fastened to the bed for five days to keep her still, and then had to have bed-rest for six weeks when she came home. Birmingham was surrounded by barrage balloons, so the doctor came to see Mom at home, to save her travelling in case all the traffic stopped because of an air raid.

The only thing I remember about St Michael's is they would accept my Mom for a week, or fortnight, so we could go on holiday, as she suffered from arthritis. Years ago it was known as the workhouse.

Mrs J. Yates

My mother was admitted to Victoria Hospital on 21 December and had an 18 week stay on the female ward.

I remember helping her to make snowmen and snowballs, using cotton wool and toilet roll bases in the run up to Christmas.

On New Year's Day in 1946, the Lichfield Trent Valley train accident occurred. The New Year celebrations faded. A London-bound express fish train ploughed into the back of a passenger train, consisting of very old wooden coaches, waiting in the station. Twenty were killed and many more were injured.

I remember going in to visit and seeing piles of salvaged clothing and effects lying on both sides of the corridors and cries of anguish and pain from the injured could be heard.

A 10 year old girl called Brenda from London occupied the bed next to my mother. The child was very distressed, so much so that her bed was pushed right up to my mother's so that Mom could try to pacify her. Brenda's stay on the ward amounted to some weeks, so that over visiting times we got to know her, as well as her aunt and uncle who lived in Streethay. In due course, by way of showing their appreciation, Brenda's aunt and uncle gave us a lovely Golden Retriever puppy.

In those days the surgeons, GPs and all hospital staff did sterling work. Major surgery was divided between the Vic, Hammerwich and Tamworth hospitals. This was before the days of Good Hope and Burton District Hospitals.

Years later, I joined the Lichfield detachment of the British Red Cross and all members went to the Vic on a Sunday afternoon to make beds, give out teas and try to make ourselves useful. Later still I joined a yoga class, which was held in the basement, to raise funds for the maternity department. These are my memories.

Mrs J. Simmons

Probationer nurses were taken in residence at the Vic at the age of sixteen. Miss Cant had a master key that enabled her to moderate domestic order in their bedrooms, by spot checking them. One day, Miss Cant had spotted an outrageously untidy probationer room, and was incensed enough to find the offending girl, call her away from her duties and escort her back to her room. She flung wide the door with an imperious, 'Nurse, what is the meaning of ....' The sight of the immaculately tidy room that lay before her silenced Miss Cant. The bush telegraph must have been fully functional that day!

Vera Burbridge

When I was about 10 years old, in 1953, I went into Hammerwich Hospital to have my tonsils out. I was put in the men's ward. The patients and the nurses were very good to me.

On the day I was going home I went round to say goodbye. I shook their hands and they each put a sixpence in my hand. It's something I have never forgot. They had treated me so good I didn't want to leave.

Mr W. A. Cheshire

I used to live in Tamworth Street. My eldest son was born in April 1956 at St Michael's. Wonderful care was given and one particular midwife who I recall was Sister Spraggalt, who came from Shenstone.

My daughter was born at the Victoria in May 1960. It was a friendly efficient maternity unit, in the capable hands of Sister Edith Harding from Burntwood, a large lady with equally large hands, and a superb midwife. I remember that the midwife who delivered my daughter was Sister Shakespeare. My youngest son was also born at the Victoria in 1964. Most of the same staff was there. Dr Wigmore from Burntwood was our consultant.

Hammerwich Hospital was another small, much used and friendly hospital, which I frequented for out-patient clinics (by this time I had moved to Chase Terrace). Mr Hingerani, the Ear Nose and Throat consultant, came to Hammerwich, thus saving me a journey to Burton. I had numerous sessions in the physio department.

Mrs Joyce Woodings

Michael Elsom recalls two colourful characters who served St Michael's Hospital for many years. Alf Mears was without arms, but found this no deterrent to providing a first-class service. He would arrive at work in the Chest Unit, remove his shoes and socks, and operate the switchboard with his toes. Albert Edward Sperrin served St Michaels' as Head Gardener for many years, and was the owner of a black Ford Prefect. He was also a self-styled Lichfield poet, with his work frequently gracing the pages of the *Mercury* in honour of whatever auspicious occasion.

The actual architecture of the Vic made it a quiet, impressive building. It stood about 50 yards from the main road. The walk up the drive, with well-tended front gardens and the path, led to the large front door with its well-polished brass furniture. As a young girl, **Sheri Corbett** walked past the Vic many times from her own home to that of her grandparents. Once her parents felt she was old enough to be trusted to do the walk on her own, it marked a rite of passage in Sheri's life. To her, 'It always looked so solid and enduring nestled in its pleasant grounds.' The foregrounds of the Vic were also the backdrop for the annual Boxing Day Hunt that gathered in front of the Bowling Green. The red brick of the hospital was a perfect background to show off the colours donned by equestrians, the shining coats of the horses and hounds, the brass of the hunt's trumpet, all together making a splendid spectacle. One year, the huntsmen had to work extra hard to rally the hounds, as it was a bright sunny morning, and the veranda doors were open on the male ward. The hounds made their way in, and found no reason to leave in a hurry because of the biscuits and tit-bits offered them by the patients.

My nostalgic memories revolve around the Victoria Hospital, Lichfield in 1966. My son was born in January of that year at the hospital, and my dear father passed away in October of the same year – the exact date in that year as this letter is being written, coincidentally.

In those days only the husband was allowed to visit mother and newborn baby during the 10 day stay at the hospital. Later in the year when my father was admitted, baby wasn't allowed to visit with me.

So, to enable grandfather to see his only grandson, I carried my baby round to the gardens at the rear of the hospital to a convenient window where we could be seen from my father's hospital bed, to wave a fond farewell.

I'm certain there were very sensible precautions taken, and all three of us during our stay at the Victoria were well cared for. I was sorry in later years to see the hospital close and later demolished. Our doctor at that time – Dr Marshall – was I believe, one of the founder members of the hospital.

Mrs P.D. Done

I was seven years old and after having suffered from various sore throats it was decided that the time had come for me to have my tonsils removed. I was told that I would have to go to hospital to be operated on. There were many pats on the head and reassuring smiles, all very well meant, but I sensed that there was something slightly threatening about the whole situation.

The appointed day arrived and I remember walking to the hospital, with Grandma and with a new dolly in my arms. That was nice, but getting a new dolly did seem slightly suspicious. As we entered the building, it was as if we had come into a new world. The first thing that hit my senses was the omnipresent smell of disinfectant. There was a brisk but friendly air about the nurses in their strange dress. I was allotted my bed in a women's ward and after Grandma had left I was shown around the other wards by a nice nurse. This was probably to put me at my ease, but I was slightly embarrassed by the sight of so many strange men in their pyjamas in the men's ward.

The only negative recollection I have is of waking up in the night after the operation. My throat was sore, I could taste blood and the smell of the rubber sheeting I was lying on made me feel nauseous. Also I was very thirsty. I was soon being attended to and comforted and was given ice-cubes wrapped in gauze to quench my thirst.

There was a funny encounter with the visiting doctor on his rounds, in the company of other members of the staff. He stood at the bedside and asked questions in a language I didn't understand, about bowel movement and the state of my bladder. I somehow managed to imagine what he was talking about and replied that I had 'done a wee-wee' if that was what he meant, to the amusement of all present.

On the whole I can say that I actually enjoyed my stay in hospital. It was nice to be pampered, the staff and other patients were very kind. I was given lots of ice-cream to eat and was the centre of attention for a while.

The Victoria Hospital remains in my memory as a special place where I was looked after in the best sense. And I still like the smell of disinfectant to this day!

Cynthia Schmid

In the late 1960s I worked in the Salaries and Wages Department at Burton for the Burton Hospital Management Committee. I am not sure if St Matthew's Hospital was part of the HMC or if it was just supplied with a payroll service.

In those days large numbers of staff were paid weekly and in cash. Every Friday morning it would be 'all hands to the pump' as everyone in our department, with other staff drafted in to help, worked in pairs to put together all the weekly pay-packets for the various hospitals. Thousands of pounds of cash were delivered first thing by Securicor.

Late morning I was taken to St Matthew's by Securicor with a large locked steel box containing the pay packets for that hospital. Two 'pay parades' were held, one just before lunch at mid-day I think, and the other at 2.00 p.m. In between time I usually had a very nice lunch in the hospital canteen, which had waitress service in those days, and a quick drink in the hospital's sports and social club.

During the pay parade, staff would identify themselves and then sign to say they had received their pay packet which I had handed to them.

I recall that both pay parades were held in the hospital gymnasium and the second was usually more interesting as most weeks some form of patient activity, such as dancing, started at the same time!

Roy Wheeldon

Do you believe in coincidence? My tale may make you reconsider. It is my story of my association with Lichfield Victoria Hospital.

In October 1963 I was married to a Lichfield man and we bought a house and moved to Hammerwich. In August 1964 I found myself pregnant with our first baby. Our son David was born on 19 April 1965 at the Victoria Hospital. I had gone into labour on the Saturday evening and was admitted to the maternity unit in the early hours of Sunday morning. As it was Easter Sunday the maternity unit was empty apart from me. I was 20 years old at the time and was quite anxious and afraid at what was to happen.

The rain had started on Saturday and by the time I was admitted to maternity a thunderstorm was raging overhead. Back in those days husbands were not encouraged to stay with their wives, and I found myself alone in what I remember as a four or five bed ward. I remember spending time watching the thunder and lightening through the window. I don't recall much activity until my waters broke and I was asked to walk to the delivery room. I remember thinking the loud thunder seemed to make the whole experience unreal. My son David Alan Davies was born at 6.25 a.m. on Easter Sunday.

I remember babies were not left with their mothers but wheeled in for feeding and changing times, then taken back to the nursery. Breast feeding was the order of the day and I remember our son having a problem feeding. A lovely nurse (sorry, I can't recall her name) said that he was short-tongued, but she cut the little bit of skin under his tongue and then he was able to feed normally. My memory of this incident was that she had undertaken to do this without the knowledge of the doctor.

Nurses were overshadowed by doctors. My baby was wheeled to the side of my bed when visitors came. Only two per bed were allowed and no sitting on the bed was allowed! We were not encouraged to take the baby out of the cot. The whole process was so different from today – almost regimented, as everything was done in a set manner.

My story moves ahead to 40 years minus one day. I was working for the NHS and, due to the closure of the practice I was working at, I was transferred to the Lichfield Victoria Hospital to work at the Locality Office. My transfer date was 18 April 2005. On the following day, 19 April, my son's 40th birthday, I found myself standing at the window looking out over the hospital while watching a thunderstorm. It was a very real and somewhat weird experience to be in the same place, during a thunderstorm, as I had been 40 years before.

Margaret Hoult

My memories of Hammerwich Hospital:

The principal instigators were George Hodgkins who lived in the toll house at what became Anchor Bridge of High Street, Brownhills, about 50-100 yards from where I was born in 1927; and George Bradbury of the drapers, High Street, Brownhills; and I believe Vic Fenn, a mine owner of Chasetown.

It was built before my time with the money provided by the people of Brownhills and Chasetown, Hammerwich, etc. It was built for their own benefit mainly and became a project that everyone was pleased and proud of.

I was never an in-patient, but enjoyed numerous kinds of help there: X-rays, physio, and a bad cut stitched up. My mother, sister, wife and her sister had their tonsils out there.

In the 1960s and 1970s, Hammerwich had numerous clinics where specialists saw local people, saving them the worry of travelling miles to be helped. They cannot enjoy this now, since Hammerwich Hospital was stolen from them.

I am not sorry to say that because it's true and the locals have also lost the feeling of security once so admirably provided. I believe this is called progress by the government.

E. A. Downes

An excerpt from the transcript of former nurses in conversation:

Pat Wain: I started at the Victoria Hospital in 1967, but before that, for a six month period, I worked at Barton Cottage Hospital. And that was a big difference for me having come from a teaching hospital. I lived in Alrewas and I used to get the red bus down the

A38 and I left my bike at one of those little cottages at Barton Turns and the reason I left there was that someone stole the wheels from my bicycle. I then had an interview with Miss Cant at the Victoria Hospital and I was successful in the position of Sister in the out-patients department where I stayed for five years.

The things that I remember most and the things that I value most from my experience were meeting so many people in Lichfield, but it was just such a happy experience and environment working with the consultants...some of them no longer with us, people like Dr Eddy and Mr Chatha and Dr Gibbs who was wonderful and my favourite Mr Frank Hurford.

Angela Reynolds: We had a particularly poorly patient and were very concerned about him and he was obviously going to die. But he was always so relaxed, so easy and calm about it all, and I can remember saying to Mr Hurford, 'How can he just accept it like this?' and he said, 'Reynolds, the Almighty draws a veil over their understanding.'

Pat Wain: We always had to leave a cigarette in his packet after he had finished seeing his patients...he lit the cigarette and I forget what we were doing, but we had thrown some cotton wool swabs in the bin with meths on, and he threw the match into the bin and of course the whole thing went up in flames. And he then got up and was shaking his leg because his trousers had caught on fire. And he said, 'I'm going to have to take my trousers off!'

June Buckle: It was the consultants that actually started to talk to us junior nurses, I mean we weren't even allowed to acknowledge the GPs at all, unless we were spoken to.

Angela Reynolds: You're right because I remember when they came round to do their rounds – they wore white coats. And we always had to stand there like minions and hold the doctor's white coat.

My Great Auntie Violet died in the Victoria Hospital. I don't know how old she was, as she was always old to me. She lived next door to where I grew up as a child; she was my grandmother's sister. She was buxom and cuddly and always willing to play. She had the best button tin in the world and I would spend hours emptying it onto the kitchen floor and playing with the buttons. She had lots of knitting needles and was always ready to play pick-up sticks.

Great Auntie Violet left the country and went to live with her daughter and granddaughters in Rhodesia. Many years later she came back. She eventually settled in Holbrooke House in Lichfield. People who knew her would probably not recognise her from my description, as she could be outspoken, irascible and opinionated, maybe. But she was constant and loving to me.

She fell ill. She was admitted to the Victoria Hospital, where she had a lovely, sunny room. She sat in bed waiting for her daughter to come from Zimbabwe so she could say goodbye, refusing to die until she had seen her. Looking out of the window onto the garden, she asked me if I could see the lovely colours of the peacocks parading on the lawn outside. She was smiling and waiting. The following day her daughter came and she said goodbye. I miss her.

Adele Montgomery

I started at St Matthew's Hospital on 24 August 1972. My friend begged me to go with her as there were three vacancies for seamstresses. The sad part was I got the job and she didn't. So I felt awful about it. I had to go and tell her, but later on she got a job at another hospital. I was very pleased for her.

I worked on a sewing machine 40 hours a week. We used to make curtains for hospitals as well as clinics, uniform alterations for nurses and all the repairs for patients and staff. Some of the patients had been there for years.

We used to go on the wards to take some of the repairs back. On a Friday afternoon we would cut up old clothing for dusters for the cleaners.

Then they decided to close the hospital. I was lucky because you could only work until 65, so I retired after working 21 years there, but I enjoyed it.

Mrs Barbara Cater

I am writing to say that I had all four of my children at the Victoria Hospital between 1968 and 1980, three daughters and a son. The staff at the Vic looked after us excellently. I would not have gone anywhere else. The friendliness was second to none.

The Vic staff were a very good team.

Pam Fairfield

Mrs Pat Staniford used to be a PE teacher and swimming coach in Tamworth. However during her early teaching career she developed bi-polar disorder, which occasionally required admission into an acute mental health unit. Despite her condition, she recalls many happy events during her repeated stays at St Matthew's. It was 'free – lots of grassy areas and trees'. She even compared it to a holiday camp!

During 1978 she was admitted to the mixed ward for a series of treatments involving electro-convulsive therapy (ECT). The camaraderie between the patients at St Matthew's was 'like 4th year students at a secondary school'.

A present-day nurse at George Bryan Centre concurs:

> I was the ECT nurse who met the patients when they arrived. The driver of the van was a porter who inexplicably donned a white coat on ECT mornings, they usually wore brown coats. After the ECT session all patients were offered tea and toast before going back on the van for the return trip to the wards and, yes, a certain camaraderie developed and veterans would take care of new patients. Some of our sessions were for 17 patients so it was a very busy department.

Usually the treatment consisted of a series of six ECT treatments. An injection was given before the ECT to ensure that the patient was relaxed. This did not hurt at all and generally after the six treatments received Mrs Staniford knew she felt better. In fact she was fully recovered. This feeling was shared by many other fellow patients.

If there is a current need for her to be admitted to an acute mental health unit again, she stays in the George Bryan Centre in Tamworth. When she does, she meets many familiar faces as a good number of the nurses were students at the time when she stayed in St Matthew's. True continuity of care...

Nurses have traditionally provided care around the clock, and taken their share in night duty. It was the pattern at St Michael's for one break during the night to be a sleeping break, during which the nurse could go to a quiet room upstairs for one hour to close her eyes. A colleague would invariably come upstairs and knock at the door to tell you that your hour's break was finished. One nurse recounts her extraordinary experience:

In the early 1980s, I had not been long on nights and was frightened that I might not wake up from my sleeping break. I and two colleagues were sent upstairs at 3 a.m. for our sleeping break. I lined up some chairs next to the wall, and stretched myself out on the chairs with my cape for a blanket. I fell asleep readily. While asleep I sensed a bright light, the wall had 'disappeared' and I was being woken by a young nurse in a lilac uniform bending over me, telling me it was time to wake up. I woke to find the room was still in darkness and my colleagues still resting.

After a while, we were all woken by one of our night-time colleagues to say that our break was finished. Returning to duty, I told my experience to a colleague who had worked at St Michael's for some years and knew the hospital and its buildings well. She informed me that years ago, student nurses at St Michael's wore lilac...

An older colleague used to cycle from Burntwood to St Michael's in Lichfield for her night shifts. At one point her bike may have been stolen or wrecked (I can't fully recall due to the passage of time), which caused her great difficulty with transport to and from work. Her colleagues put money together to surprise her with a brand new bike. One night, having taken our night duty handover and settled our patients to sleep, we presented our colleague with her new cycle. She was so excited that in the early hours of the morning, she tried it out by cycling the full length of the Nightingale wards including the corridor that joined them. Patients were sleeping soundly, or so we thought. Next morning, while washing our patients, two of them wondered if they'd been dreaming, because they had seen a nurse riding a bicycle up and down the ward!

We used to have some awful jobs really but they were quite interesting. And I remember we had this old lady admitted and I remember we undressed her, and she had a body belt on. She had a thousand pounds in old notes in this thing. And it absolutely reeked, and we got someone to go down to the bank with these smelly old notes, which were her life savings.

It was these eccentrics that made life fun. They just don't make them like that anymore. Wonderful.

And do you remember the ferret man? He used to come in quite regularly and he would come and visit from time to time with a couple of dead rabbits slung around his neck. He came in one Christmas morning. He had a dead duck under his arm, and he'd taken it off the pool! And an enterprising nurse took it and dressed it and put it in the freezer!

Angela Reynolds

Joyce Wood ('Woody') came to the rescue on one occasion when a younger nurse colleague was terrified to go to the Mortuary, which was a separate building in the Victoria Hospital grounds:

> As nurses we had been deemed competent to verify death if the patient was expected to die. I had only done this for the first time, had performed Last Offices, and had the patient moved to the Mortuary. Some hours later, the porter came and said he could hear a knocking sound coming from within the Mortuary. Horrified that I may have got things terribly wrong, I sent

Woody to investigate. To all of our relief, when she opened the Mortuary door, a pigeon flew out!

Helen Russell

On 14 December 1983 I gave birth to my second son at the Victoria Hospital. Edward was two weeks early and came out as a little screwed-up, jaundiced baby with a mass of spiky black hair. The 'in', must-have toy at the time was the Cabbage Patch doll and I remarked that my baby Edward looked like one. But an older midwife overheard what I said and rebuked me sharply, saying that all babies were beautiful and that I should not have made such a remark about my baby.

Edward is now a very good-looking young man, but looking back at a photo of him when he was born, I still say he looked like a Cabbage Patch doll.

Mrs S. Hobday

Memories of the Vic:

Some years ago, it was necessary for me to have surgery and I had experience of three hospitals over a period of nine months. However, I recall how lovely it was to return home to our dear Vic prior to my final convalescence and restoration to health. I received nothing but kindness in this small, friendly hospital with beautifully cooked and appetising meals. The atmosphere was warm and welcoming with ease of access for family and friends.

I also call to mind a number of other incidents where the reaction was 'take her to the Vic'; for example, a nasty scald on the arm, making coffee for breakfast one Sunday morning when the percolator slipped, or a bad nose bleed one Christmas. There was also an occasion when a friend from Canada was staying and became violently sick after eating mussels – she was cared for at the Vic.

E.F.

Wakey, Wakey!

Six o'clock and the lights all go up
Morning tea or coffee, there for us to sup.
The rattle of trolleys and thermometer machines
Nurses start chattering, another day begins.

Bed pans and wash bowls all come into sight,
Tablets dispensed; after checking they're right.
Beds made with clean sheets.....and put straight,
For now it is breakfast, the time, it's just eight.

Doctors and registers surge into view
With results of X-rays and instruments anew.
Ten o'clock, mid morning drinks are now here.
Phone ringing, buzzers buzzing, more bed pans I fear.

Patients are wheeled out of sight for their scans,
Nurses all busy, keeping up with demands
Of patients and Doctors and 'Things right away'
What's that you're saying? It's now lunch and midday!

Anne (former patient of the Victoria and Hammerwich Hospitals)

I remember the Victoria Hospital back in 1988.

It was the year my daughter Stacey was born. The staff and midwives were really nice and friendly to me, and helped me a lot – they even had bets on me giving birth on Christmas Day. They all lost; I ended up giving birth on 21 December.

As far as I can remember, there was another woman in the ward with me. The hospital was quiet at the time; there was a Christmas tree by the side of my bed, and the atmosphere was lovely. The local vicar came and blessed both my daughter and me. I was allowed home on Christmas Eve.

The midwife who delivered my daughter was Sister Walker. It could not have been a bad place as I was back again in 1991, when I gave birth to a baby boy, Martin, again delivered by Sister Walker.

The Victoria Hospital was a great part of the community for the City of Lichfield; being born in it myself, it was nice to have my children born there too. I will always remember the Vic fondly.

Mrs Julie Gough

Dot, having undergone renal dialysis at the Vic for many years, gave this letter of her memories to Helen Bishop, Sister of the Renal Unit:

My name is Dot and I have been on the renal unit at the Victoria Hospital, Lichfield, since it opened in 1988. The nursing staff have been good to me over the years. They were always playing tricks on us.

One day we were given salad for lunch and found flies in it, which the nurses had put there. Another time a patient called Percy was in the lift and found some dog muck, which made him sick, but when told by the nurses that it was only artificial, he still swore that he could smell it. Once a patient fell asleep and when he woke up thought that he had gone blind because the nurses had put tape over his glasses.

In the early 1990s the nurses, Maureen, Linda and Gay, took me and some other patients to Majorca, which was financed by doing car boot sales and jumble sales. I also did a sponsored walk around Tamworth athletic stadium, walking miles. We also did a couple of race nights and raised a lot of money, thanks to Lyn's husband who worked very hard. My husband and I have been on holiday to Majorca a few times, but we always remember the first time with the nurses and patients with fondness. I hope that when we move to the new unit at the Samuel Johnson Hospital it will give us as many happy times as we had at the Victoria Hospital. I will miss it very much.

Dot Broadbent

(Sadly, Dot died in June 2009. She is remembered with great fondness by the Renal Unit team who miss her. Sister Bishop stated that Dot became the 'matriarch' of the unit, having attended for 21 years.)

On a quiet Sunday morning in September in the early 1990s I was the staff nurse on Casualty duty with Sister Hickinbotham. We were in the reception area awaiting the first patients of the day. A pleasant gentleman arrived at the counter, and asked if he could be seen by a nurse. I recognised his face from many photographs in the *Mercury* as the incumbent Sheriff of Lichfield. Sister Hickinbotham stepped forward to register his personal details. Having noted his surname and first name, she asked, 'What's happened?' 'I injured my ankle whilst horse-riding yesterday,' he replied, to which Sister H.

pronounced emphatically, 'I hope you weren't doing that stupid Sheriff's Ride!' 'Occupation?' she went on to ask. He kept a straight face: 'Sheriff.'

Mary Hutchinson

Gerry Wilson was a member of staff on the renal ward and sent a letter relating her own humorous experience:

Early in the year of 2001, I was coming to the end of a long 12 to 12 shift. At approximately 11.30 p.m., I went into the staff changing room, as I needed to go to the toilet. When I was ready to leave the toilet, I tried to unlock the door, but the lock broke and then I found that the door would not open. I was not worried, as I knew that the other two members of staff on the same shift would have to come into the changing room. I thought that if this was going to happen to anyone, it would be me, as I seem to attract this sort of thing.

When the other two members of staff came into the changing room, I called to them. We all started laughing (with me still locked in the toilet), then one of the staff said not to laugh, as I might be upset and panicking. I was thinking that they might need to call the fire brigade and a young hunky fireman could rescue me. But it was not to be. They called the security man, who had only started working at the Victoria Hospital three hours earlier that night. He came and twisted the handle, etc., with no success. We never saw him again. Maybe the job was too stressful!

I then looked out the window and saw a very narrow flat roof, so I placed a chair (which just happened to be in the toilet) out of the window, climbed out of the window and walked along the roof. The other nurses had opened the next window, which led into the locker area, where I climbed in bringing the chair with me!

A note was put on the notice board on the renal unit for the following morning to let Colin Perry (the plant room engineer) know that the lock was broken on the staff toilet door. Colin went into the toilet the way I had come out, to check that I was not still in there!

From then on one of the patients always called me Lou Lou!

When I came on duty the following afternoon, although it wasn't said who got locked in the toilet, the staff had looked who was on duty the previous night and said straight away it must be me! For me, however, I was very disappointed not to have been rescued by a young, handsome, hunky fireman!
Gerry Wilson

One morning at the Lichfield factory where I worked, there were several comments from other fellow workers regarding the way a colleague, Danny, was behaving. 'Oh look at Danny, he's acting funny again!' On hearing some of these friendly jibes of concern, I glanced over to where Danny was working. Being concerned at the state I saw Danny in, I went running over to help:

I couldn't believe my eyes – Danny was sitting on a chair with his head hanging down, his legs were stretched out and he was just muttering. Trying to say something but he couldn't say anything properly. I knew straight away what was wrong with Danny...he had previously told us that he suffered from diabetes and had to take insulin to keep it under control.

The fact that I also had a problem with diabetes heightened my concern for Danny. Although I had Type II diabetes and was not dependent on insulin, I knew that by the way he was acting, his sugar levels had dropped very low. This was the reason why Danny had no idea of what he was doing or saying. In haste to get some sugar into him, I quickly got a couple of chocolate bars from the vending machine and tried to make him eat them. But it did not make any difference.

I went and told my team leader at that time. We found the First Aid leader and explained Danny's situation to her. It was decided to give a solution of sugar and water to Danny, in hope that it might alleviate his crisis, but to no avail. Danny was seen to be deteriorating, so we took him straight to the Vic.

Danny had a blood test. When the nurses checked his blood sugar level, it was unbelievable – 1.5 mmol/l. The nurses quickly gave him a high dose injection of glucose. It took about 30 minutes to bring Danny round.

As the nurses were trying to coax Danny back to consciousness, he threatened, 'Don't mess with me, I'm a trained killer!' Once recovered, Danny had no recollection of what he had said and when later told of his outburst, had a good laugh about it.

Since his experience Danny checks his blood sugar level regularly and keeps it under control. From relating this story I hope that readers may learn how dangerous diabetes is. We were told if another ten or fifteen minutes had passed, Danny could have been in a serious situation.

Harjinder Kalsi

Time Off for Good Behaviour

Go for six months
Said Miss Pegg
Get experience and then
They will beg
You to come back to St Mick's.

So I went, got experience
But I really enjoyed it
So I stayed and I worked
Quite a lot, not a bit
I remained at the Vic - not St Mick's.

In casualty, I learnt how to suture,
And examine most bodily parts.
I pacified drunks and
Put cream on what bit smarts!
That's what I learnt at the Vic.

Surgery, gynae, ortho and general
On the ward was always quite busy;
Hysterectomies, hernias, bunions
Too many, we really were dizzy!
That's what we repaired at the Vic.

They helped me achieve education:
ENBs, Diploma and Degree.
I had to work hard and study
And in those days, they paid the fee.
I'm so glad I was at the Vic.

The patients, Joe, George, Hilda

Were friends, not clients or user.
Aileen and John, their families too
Were all part of the Victoria's culture
They were all at the heart of the Vic.

The staff became part of one's family.
We picked strawberries at dawn,
Partied, played and we had
Balls and cream teas on the lawn!
We enjoyed our life at the Vic.

Two hospitals merged and it all changed.
Economics? Politics? Progress?
Some staff resigned, retired, were redundant.
But then order was achieved from the mess!
And St Mick's was aligned with the Vic.

I left after twenty-five years,
To gain more experience.
I missed all the people but
I could never have sat on the fence.
I'm so glad that I worked at the Vic.

Lyn Taylor (formerly Harris)

I was an inpatient at the Vic for five months in 2004, for rehabilitation following major spinal surgery at another hospital. Due to a very serious post-operative infection I was totally dependent on others for a long time.

When I arrived at the Vic I couldn't stand, dress myself or even sit

31: David Holloway's Birthday Party

up without help. Due to the superb physiotherapy department at the Vic all that changed. I now lead a fairly normal life. I need sticks to get around, but I have my independence and can drive my car.

The nursing staff at the Vic were marvellous. They did everything for me when I first arrived. They were always cheerful in spite of being always, so it seemed, overworked. Despite this there was always the highest standard of care for patients.

I had a birthday whilst there and I remember it was a glorious hot sunny day. My family arrived along with lots of friends and the staff allowed us to hold a party on the terrace outside the ward. They provided trays of teas and coffees and joined in singing 'Happy Birthday', as well as making me a very special birthday card (which I still have), from 'The Angels of the Night'.

My feeling about the Vic is that it had a real heart, emanating from the staff and the memories that they all had. Many were old hands at nursing (and had been at the Vic for a long time). They knew what was required to make life as good as possible for everyone and especially for long-stay patients like me.

I know many people were saddened when the Vic was bulldozed to make way for housing, believing that no new hospital could provide the Heart of the old Vic!

Mr David Holloway

This chapter could never be complete – there are so many rich memories of the hospitals that have served the people of Lichfield and surrounding villages. However we hope readers find this sample sufficient to give them insight into times past and an understanding of the values that these hospitals brought to all who knew them.

Conclusion

Our narrative and anecdotal history of the hospitals that served Lichfield and district over the past 150 years is now complete. It is a rich story of political evolution, individual and group philanthropy, and the contribution of many local citizens, for the good of all.

Many factors influence health care delivery today, and challenge our ability to maintain the National Health Service principle of health care free at the point of need for UK citizens. Fundamental changes in the roles and responsibilities of health care professionals and the relationship between clinicians and patients are vital if the NHS is going to meet the future challenges of an aging population, of more informed and demanding patients, and of an increase in chronic disease. Greater understanding of the human genome will provide individually sensitive and specific information, enabling doctors to diagnose, prevent or treat more diseases.

The concept of putting patient need and choice at the heart of the NHS is a major policy objective. The dynamics of the market-place are being actively encouraged as primary care commissioning is handed over to General Practitioners to choose health care for their local population from diverse private and public health care providers. Eventually the public will be able to access their NHS Care Records themselves, and be more involved in making decisions about their own care and treatment. Modern technology offers the vision of more readily available data through diverse options, for example:

- The National Programme for Information Technology will enable an electronic 'spine' of patient information accessible to most clinicians in most places.

- The Picture Archiving and Communication System (PACS) enables images such as X-rays and scans to be stored electronically and viewed on screens, so that doctors and other health professionals can access the information and compare it with previous images at the touch of a button, wherever they work.

- Bluetooth technology enables data to be transmitted from sensors attached to a person's body directly to a computer. Electronic data will be able to trigger treatment like insulin release, or implantable heart monitors will be able to transmit information directly to a GP in the surgery so that clinical decisions can be made far away from the patient.

However brave this new world may be, there will always be need of skilled medical and nursing interventions when people become unwell for whatever reason.

As Care in the Community became a political driver in health care in the late 1980s, St Matthew's Hospital's services to the mentally ill and elderly were curtailed; by the mid-1990s the buildings and land were sold for future development. However, the 'patient-led' standard of monitoring the quality of care that was practised in its heyday as the County Lunatic Asylum would stand muster with the Care Quality Commission of today.

The local press records much controversy about the suggested closure of the Lichfield and Burntwood hospitals during the late 20th century, though health care managers promised that the city would never lose the services of a community hospital. Sandra Walker, then Director of Operations of Burntwood, Lichfield and Tamworth Primary Care Trust, became project manager of the proposed new community hospital and worked tirelessly to ensure that the community hospital services upon which Lichfield and

Burntwood had come to rely would be perpetuated in the 21st century. In the Department of Health document, *Transforming Community Services* (2009), bringing acute care closer to home is seen as a contemporary measure to reduce unnecessary and expensive admission to large acute hospitals.

As evidence that the quality of care remains undiluted in our new community hospital, two members of staff were awarded Community Hospital Association Awards for Innovations and Best Practice in Community Hospitals in May 2010.

First, Helen Giles, Team Leader/Ward Manager of the Maternity Unit explains her role:

> The brand new and purpose built stand alone midwife-led unit is part of the Samuel Johnson Community Hospital. The unit replaced an old but much loved building. The first step in designing and planning the new unit was to ask the local community and service users what they wanted. Ideas and suggestions flooded in. A strong vision emerged that the women wanted to take the homeliness from the old unit but to have access to more modern and up-to-date facilities. The staff wanted a more practical, efficient and ergonomic space to work. The challenge was to combine the two within the plethora of legislation that now exists for a new build!
>
> Eighteen months later we moved in exhausted, excited and somewhat apprehensive. On opening day we breathed a huge sigh of relief, all our hard work had come to fruition and everybody said, 'wow, we love it'. The first baby was born within hours of opening and from then we have gone from strength to strength. We are now in our third year and more women are accessing our service and the number of births has increased to

32: Sandra Walker in the Boardroom of the Vic

over 400 for the first time. The facilities include two birthing pools. Currently 40% of births at the unit occur in water. Our aim is to provide individual, personalised care. This enables women to feel confident in the birthing process and helps them make decisions about their care.

And secondly, Anne Rogers, Renal Dietitian, describes her award-winning work:

As a dietitian taking on a new role in a Community Hospital Haemodialysis Unit, I realised not only the importance of increasing my own knowledge and skills to ensure good patient care, but the importance of both listening to the individual needs of patients as well as understanding the positive impact that dietetic intervention can have from a renal nurse perspective. As a result I decided to plan an education program to help patients better manage the dietary restrictions necessitated by kidney failure and dialysis.

Discussions with the nursing team highlighted key areas of concern relating to the importance of on-going verbal, written and practical dietary advice. All patients receive appropriate tailored dietary advice initially, but finding new ways to encourage, remind and individualise advice is a constant challenge. This is clearly not a project of finite duration but an on-going process of advising and helping patients to make appropriate choices to optimise both their short and long term health.

Lichfield is blessed to have the new Samuel Johnson Community Hospital to provide its diverse services through our lives. In the spirit of the hospitals that have served the citizens of Lichfield and surrounding villages in the past, it is truly well-placed to offer care closer to home.

33: Samuel Johnson Community Hospital

Acknowledgements

The idea for this book arose back in 2005 when Primary Care Trust staff were asked to think of ways to raise funds to equip the new community hospital, to be erected on the site of the former St Michael's Hospital. Our idea was to write a book that would tell the human story of the Victoria Hospital; profits from the sale would be given to the new community hospital.

A few willing friends agreed to help with the project, and met to form the Lichfield Hospitals History Group. A debt of gratitude is owed to the Lichfield Conduit Land trustees for their generous financial support that has enabled production of this book. In addition, we would wish to acknowledge the contribution made by Jonathan Wait of F.M. & J. Wait.

Early in our work, it became apparent that former staff of the Victoria Hospital had also worked in both Hammerwich and St Michael's Hospitals, and sometimes St Matthew's as well; their histories were closely intertwined. In addition, compelling as these human stories were, they needed to be set in the context of time and place. Therefore, the group decided it was best to tell the story of each of these hospitals.

It was an honour to meet Ellen Leighfield, who had written an earlier history of both the Victoria (1983) and St Michael's (1978) Hospitals. We are grateful to her for having been willing to share her work, which has provided the foundation for the chapters relating to these hospitals. David Budden, former pharmacist at St Matthew's, wrote *A County Lunatic Asylum: The History of St. Matthew's Hospital, Burntwood* (1989). He has kindly agreed to the inclusion of parts of his work in our chapter on St Matthew's. Thanks are also due to Laura Bowcutt who generously gave her time and provided photographs from her days as a student nurse at St Matthew's Hospital. Angela Reynolds, former nursing sister at the Vic, Principal Lecturer in the School of Health, University of Wolverhampton and now an independent educationalist, has provided information, inspiration and guidance.

Dr Jeremy Duncan-Brown and Dr Elizabeth Muller kindly provided historical information relating to general practitioners who have served the hospitals down the years. All of the above contributed greatly to the successful exhibition, 'A Century of Service' that was held in St Mary's Centre in 2007.

Our thanks go to the many former workers (nurses, administrators, volunteers and others) who have recounted their memories of working in the hospitals, and to local citizens who have shared their stories – giving a human voice to our history.

Three people deserve special acknowledgement for giving their professional expertise so generously. Marty Smith has kindly proof-read and copy-edited the text. Jayne Wilson has brought her graphic art skills to bear in creating the cover and layout of this book. Martin Wilson has helped with production and marketing.

Mary Hutchinson, Ingrid Croot and Anna Sadowski

Lichfield Hospitals History Group:

Mary Baker	Arthur Hutchinson
Ingrid Croot	Mary Hutchinson
Dr Ayliffe Edwards	Stephen Sanders
Les Fox	Martin Wilson

References

Preface
Kerr, A., 2001. Hospital Round-up. *Lichfield Mercury,* 11 Oct. p.3.

Chapter 1

Aronson, S.M., 2004. *Leprosy: a Disease of the Soul.*
Medicine and Health Rhode Island (online) Available at:
http://findarticles.com (Accessed: 23 Oct 09).

Dainton, C., 1961. *The Story of England's Hospitals.* London:
Museum Press Ltd.

Encyclopaedia Britannica, 2009. (online) Available at:
http://www.britannica.com (Accessed: 6 Dec 09).

Erasmus Darwin House. 2010. *Celebrating the Amazing Dr Darwin*
(online) Available at: http://www.erasmusdarwin.org/history
(Accessed 26 Jan 10).

Kerr, A., 2001. Hospital Round-up. *Lichfield Mercury,* 11 Oct. p.3.

Singer, C., 2006. *A Short History of Medicine.* Oxford: Clarendon
Press.

Upton, C., 2001. *A History of Lichfield.* Chichester: Phillimore.

Victoria County History, Volume 14, 1990. *Lichfield: Parish
Government and Poor Relief; Lichfield: Public Services.* (online)
Available at: http://www.british-history.ac.uk (Accessed: 6 Dec
09; 26 Jan 10).

Williams, R., 2009. *St John's Hospital* (online)
Available at: http://www.stjohnslichfield.com (Accessed: 25 Jan 10).

Chapter 2

Budden, D., 1989. *A County Lunatic Asylum: The History of St Matthew's Hospital Burntwood.* Walsall: D. Budden.

Budden, D., 1990. The Lomax Affair. Comment in *The British Journal of Psychiatry,* 157, 301-2. (online) Available at: http://bjp.rcpsych.org (Accessed: 14 Feb 10).

Earle, P., 1854. Bloodletting in Mental Disorders. *The American Journal of Insanity,* X (4). (online) Available at: http://ajp.psychiatryonline.org (Accessed: 2 March 10).

Gibbs, D.D., 1969. Medical History: Sir John Floyer (1649-1734). *British Medical Journal,* 1, 242-45. (online) Available at: http://freepages.genealogy.rootsweb.ancestry.com/~floyer (Accessed: 2 March 10).

Lader, M. and Allderidge, P., 1975. *The SK & F History of British Pyschiatry 1700 to the Present.* Welwyn Garden City: Smith Kline and French Laboratories Ltd.

Lichfield District Council, 1998. *Local plan: Burntwood area policy B.16.* (online) Available at: http://www.lichfielddc.gov.uk (Accessed: 14 Feb 10).

National Schizophrenia Fellowship, 2009. *Care in the Community.* (online) Available at: http://www.rethink.org/livingwithmentalilllness (Accessed: Feb 10).

Staffordshire Record Office, 2007. *Burntwood Asylum.* (online) Available at: http://www.institutions.org.uk/asylums (Accessed: 14 Feb 10).

Victoria County History, Volume 14. 1990. *Lichfield: Parish Government and Poor Relief; Burntwood: Manors, Local*

Government and Public Services (online) Available at: http://www.british-history.ac.uk (Accessed: 26 Jan 10; 6 Feb 10).

Waln, R., 1825. *An Account of the Asylum for the Insane, established by the Society of Friends, near Frankford, in the Vicinity of Philadelphia*. Philadelphia: Benjamin & Thomas Kite. (online) Available at: http://www.ncbi.nlm.hih.gov/bookshelf (Accessed: 2 March 10).

Chapter 3

Multimania, 2010. *Hammerwich*. (online) Available at: http://members.multimania.co.uk/Hammerwich (Accessed: 17 March 2010).

Staffordshire County Council, 2003. *Staffordshire Places: Staffordshire & Stoke on Trent Archive Service: Hammerwich*. (online) Available at: http://www.places.staffspasttrack.org.uk (Accessed: 17 March 10).

Victoria County History, Volume 14. 1990. *Townships: Hammerwich*. (online) Available at: http://www.british history.ac.uk (Accessed: 17 March 10).

Wardropper, J., 2006. *Hospitals Built by the Owners of Industry for their Workers in Great Britain 1840-1950*. PhD dissertation: University of Birmingham. (online) Available at: http://www.rosetta.bham.ac.uk (Accessed: 6 March 10).

Chapter 4

Hansard, 1995. (online)
Available at: http://www.publications.parliament.uk (Accessed: 3 May 10).

Leighfield, E., 1983. *A History of the Victoria Hospital, Lichfield*.

Grey literature published to mark the 50th anniversary.

Victoria County History, Volume 14. 1990. *Lichfield: Public Services*. (online) Available at: http://www.british-history.ac.uk (Accessed: 30 March 10).

Wildman, S., 2009. Nursing and the Issue of 'Party' in the Church of England: the Case of the Lichfield Diocesan Nursing Association. *Nursing Inquiry*, 16(2), 94-110.

Chapter 5

Collette, C., 2009. *The Jarrow Crusade*. (online) Available at: http://www.bbc.co.uk/history/british (Accessed: 23 June 10).

De Pennington, J., 2009. *Beneath the Surface: A Country of Two Nations*. (online) Available at: http://www.bbc.co.uk/history/british (Accessed: 23 June 10).

Higginbotham, P.G., 2009. *Workhouse Food*. (online) Available at: www.workhouses.org.uk (Accessed: 23 June 10).

Higginbotham, P., 2010. *Introduction to the Workhouse Website*. (online) Available at: http://www.charlotteville.co.uk (Accessed: 23 June 10).

Chapter 6

Brown, C., 1988. *Born in a Cathedral City*. Lichfield.

Duncan-Brown, J., 2006. *Victoria Hospital Doctors*. Grey literature.

Muller, E.J., 2006. *Westgate Practice History*. Grey literature (notes extracted from a speech given at the Westgate Practice's centenary ball in March 2001; updated Nov 2006).

Obituary: T.D. Stuart Shaw, M.B., C.M. *British Medical Journal*

1960, 1:652.

Victoria County History, Volume 14. 1990. *Lichfield: Public Services.* (online) Available at: http://www.british-history.ac.uk (Accessed: 27 June 10).

Wolverhampton Archives and Local Studies, 2009. *Wolverhampton Dispensary, later South Staffordshire General Hospital and Wolverhampton Dispensary, later the Royal Hospital.* (online) Available at: http://nationalarchives.gov.uk (Accessed: 31 May 10).

Quotations

Chapter 1

Florence Nightingale, the founder of professional nursing; from *Notes on Hospitals*, 1859.

Chapter 2

Erasmus Darwin, polymath, Lunar Man and Lichfield physician; from a letter to Richard Lovell Edgeworth, 1790.

Chapter 3

Sir John Floyer, medical pioneer and Lichfield physician; from *Advice to a Young Physician*, c.1724.

Chapter 4

Joseph Addison, essayist and poet and son of the Dean of Lichfield; from *The Spectator*, 1712.

Chapter 5

Samuel Johnson, lexicographer and writer and Lichfield's most famous son; from *The Rambler*, 1750.

Chapter 6

Hester Thrale, diarist and patron of the arts and friend of Samuel Johnson; from a letter to Fanny Burney, 1781.

Chapter 7

James Boswell, friend and biographer of Samuel Johnson; from *Journal of a Tour to the Hebrides*, 1785.

Locations

 **St John's Hospital,** St John Street, Lichfield, WS13 6PB
100m west of Lichfield City Railway Station. On this site since 1135.

 **Dr Milley's Hospital,** 7 Beacon Street, Lichfield, WS13 7AA
100m west of Lichfield Cathedral Close. On this site since *c.*1424.

 **Samuel Johnson Community Hospital,** Trent Valley Road,
Lichfield, WS13 6EF
500m north-east of Lichfield City Railway Station. On the site of
Lichfield Union Workhouse (1840), later St Michael's Hospital.

 **Lichfield Victoria Nursing Home and Cottage Hospital,**
15 Sandford Street, Lichfield, WS13 6QA
Between Bird Street and Swan Road in Lichfield city centre. On
this site from 1899 to 1933.

 St Matthew's Hospital, St Matthew's Road, Burntwood, WS7 9QH
East of Burntwood town centre, 1km north of Hammerwich.
Opened 1864. Mostly demolished for housing, the administration
block and chapel have survived.

 **Lichfield Victoria Hospital,** Friary Road, Lichfield, WS13 6QN
100m south of the Bowling Green Island. Opened 1933.
Demolished in 2008 for housing.

Hammerwich Hospital, Hospital Road, Burntwood, WS7 0EH
Junction of Hospital Road and Coppy Nook Lane, 500m north
of The Triangle. Opened 1882, demolished in 2008 for housing.